BIOCHEMISTRY

Martin Carr

B.Sc., C.Biol., M.I.Biol.,
P.G.C.E., Dip. Health Ed.,
Senior Lecturer in Science,
Milton Keynes College

&

Bob Cordell

M.A., M.Ed., Senior
Lecturer and Science
Staff Tutor at the
Open University

Nelson

BIOCHEMISTRY

Thomas Nelson and Sons Ltd
Nelson House Mayfield Road
Walton-on-Thames Surrey
KT12 5PL UK

Thomas Nelson Australia
102 Dodds Street
South Melbourne
Victoria 3205 Australia

Nelson Canada
1120 Birchmount Road
Scarborough Ontario
M1K 5G4 Canada

I(T)P Thomas Nelson is an International
        Thomson Publishing Company
I(T)P is used under licence

Front cover courtesy of Science Photo Library
Illustrated by David Gardner. Cartoons by Pavely Arts

ISBN 0-17-448196-9
NPN 9 8 7 6 5 4

Printed in China

ACKNOWLEDGEMENTS

Photographic material

Hulton Picture Company p.46 (left); Science Photo Library
p.46 (right), p.58, p.107 (left and right), p.105; Cellmark
Diagnostics p.56; Rothampsted Experimental Station p.107

*The front cover shows a computer generated image of an
enzyme with details of the α- and β-chains and the
disulphide bridges.*

The authors would also like to acknowledge the help and
advice of the following: Janet Barnes, Ann Carr, Dr. Tom
Coultate and the staff of Milton Keynes Hospital Pathology
Laboratories. Finally, the authors would like to acknowledge the direct and indirect help given by their many
students. The success, as we hope, of the strategy of
biochemistry teaching in this book is due in no small
measure to their ready comment.

CONTENTS

General Editor's Introduction to the Series

Biology - Advanced Studies is a series of modular textbooks which are intended for students following advanced courses in biological subjects. The series offers the flexibility essential for working on modern syllabuses which often have core material and option topics. In particular, the books should be very useful for the new modular science courses which are emerging at A-Level.

In most of the titles in the series, one of the authors is a very experienced teacher (often also an examiner) and is sympathetic to the problems of learning at this level. The second author usually has research experience and is familiar with the subject at a higher level. In addition, several members of the writing team have been closely involved in the development of the latest syllabuses.

As with all text books, the reader may expect not to read from cover to cover but to study one topic at a time, or dip-in for information as needed. The index can be used like a science dictionary because where a page number is shown in bold print an explanation or definition will be found in the text. Where questions are asked, an attempt should be made at an answer because this type of *active reading* is the best way to develop an understanding of what is read.

We have referred throughout to *Biological nomenclature - Recommendations on terms, units and symbols,* Institute of Biology, London, 1989. We are delighted to be able to thank the many friends and colleagues who have helped with original ideas, the reading of drafts and the supply of illustrations.

Alan Cadogan

General Editor

Authors' introduction to Biochemistry

Biochemistry, at any level, is often a problem to students. This is a pity because chemical explanations play their part in *all* branches of biology. Life may be considered as consisting of nothing more than a set of chemical reactions. We are made only of chemicals and those chemicals react with each other. We are warm to touch because those reactions, like a fire, give off heat. The genetic message that was contained in the ovum of your mother and the sperm of your father was written in chemical form, i.e. the DNA of your chromosomes (see Chapter 4). The oxygen that we all breathe, perhaps two billion breaths from birth until death, is carried in chemical combination with haemoglobin to the tissues. Here it serves to oxidise the food chemicals carried to those tissues from your gut, thus providing the energy that you need to live. One chemical process after another is involved in explaining the larger scale biology that we see. In short, to answer the question that gives Chapter 1 its title, biochemistry *describes and explains the structures and processes of life in terms of chemistry.*

Many biology students have difficulty with chemistry. (The *Guide to Chemistry* will help if you are uncertain of your basic chemistry.) Even those who take advanced chemistry sometimes fail to relate the world of chemistry to the somehow 'more real' world of biology. Chapter 1 tries to put biochemistry into perspective. Do, therefore, read the chapter carefully. Don't expect to understand it all the first time you read it. Refer back to it as you take in the detail of later chapters, using Chapter 1 as an *organiser* of your biochemical knowledge. Within Chapter 1, we ask a number of questions (in boxes). These are your organisers and, by the end of the book, you should have at least partial answers. Through this approach, you will have learned all the biochemistry you need to know at this level and, more importantly, have related it to the lives of the organisms that have that biochemistry.

Martin Carr and Bob Cordell

1 BIOCHEMISTRY IS?

■ LIFE IS. . . ?

According to our definition in the introduction to the book, biochemistry is *explaining life in terms of chemistry*. Yes, but what is life? Most junior textbooks begin with a page or so listing the ***characteristics*** possessed by most living organisms, and scientists, philosophers and mystics can spend lifetimes trying to define or describe life.

Soon enough, however, most descriptions run into difficulties over viruses. These are tiny particles of nucleic acid surrounded by a protein coat. These *intracellular parasites* can do nothing except reproduce and many biologists do not regard them as living in the true sense of the word. Yet the tiny bag of protein and ribonucleic acid (RNA) (see Chapter 4) that constitutes the *HIV* virus (which causes ***AIDS***) seems alive to those who suffer from its power to destroy the human immune system. Similarly, the five million Americans with currently incurable genital herpes are all too uncomfortably aware of the liveliness of the virus that afflicts them. Even bacteria can be infected with viruses – collectively termed *bacteriophages*.

No one knows precisely how many different species inhabit the globe. New species of even large organisms, e.g. fish, trees, insects, are still discovered from time to time. And, at the bacterial and viral level, there are doubtless many more to be found, named and described. Leaving aside the viruses, there are more than two million different species currently known. These are classified, on the basis of similarities in structure, into groups of species (called genera), similar genera are in turn grouped together into families, families into orders, orders into classes and so on.

Figure 1.1 shows this idea of 'boxes within boxes', and shows the number of species in each of the five kingdoms that many biologists use.

(a)

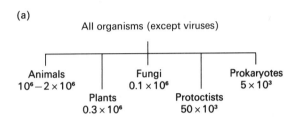

(b)

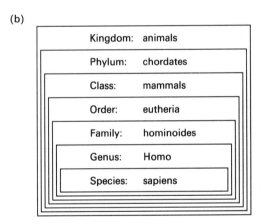

Figure 1.1 Classification of organisms. Fig. 1.1(a) shows the five kingdoms that many biologists use nowadays. Protoctists include unicellular and simple filamentous organisms of both plant-like and animal-like character. Prokaryotes include all bacteria. Fig. 1.1(b) shows the range of *taxa* (classificatory 'boxes') that biologists use. A kingdom subclassifies into phyla, a phylum into classes, etc.

---

characteristics the phenomena of nutrition, respiration, irritability, movement, excretion, reproduction and growth are those commonly listed.

AIDS acquired immune deficiency syndrome is a disease caused by the human immunodeficiency virus (HIV). Note that HIV has RNA rather than DNA such as is found in herpes virus.

Thus, you see, there is a huge range of different living organisms. But, what are their *chemical* characteristics? In terms of chemistry, what do tapeworms and elm trees have in common? What chemical differences are there between elephants and typhoid bacteria? To answer these questions, we need to look more closely at the chemical composition of organisms.

■ THE CHEMICALS OF LIFE

There is a mysterious and unbridgable gap in our knowledge of the distant past. The planet Earth was formed, evidence suggests, around 4.5 billion years before the present. Geologists, working with ancient rocks in Canada and in southern Africa, have found traces of fossil life dating from around 3.5 billion years ago. Subtracting the 'first life' date from the 'formation of the planet' date, there is a gap of about one billion years, and, somewhere in that period, the prebiotic era gave way to the biotic one, i.e. chemical systems that we would call living were created from systems that were not. Figure 1.2 shows one of the ways in which molecules that are characteristic of life have been found.

Though more will be said of the origin and evolution of life later, the following paragraphs serve to make the point that life *is* chemistry.

Of the 90 plus elements that constitute the entire universe, less than 25 are found in living organisms. Figure 1.3 shows which elements of the periodic table occur in living organisms.

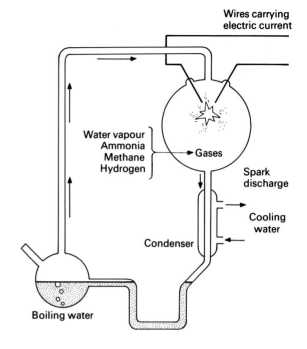

Figure 1.2   The experiment carried out in 1953 by two American scientists, Harold Urey and Stanley Miller. The boiling water in the lower flask provides water vapour — as did the warm, primitive oceans. Electric discharges into the upper flask, with its mixture of methane, ammonia and hydrogen, simulates the effect of lightning in the primordial atmosphere. Many kinds of molecule typical of life were found to accumulate in the lower flask.

I	II											III	IV	V	VI	VII	0
H																	He
Li	Be											B	C	N	O	F	Ne
Na	Mg											Al	Si	P	S	Cl	Ar
K	Ca	Sc	Ti	V	Cr	Mn	Fe	Co	Ni	Cu	Zn	Ga	Ge	As	Se	Br	Kr
Rb	Sr	Y	Zr	Nb	Mo	Tc	Ru	Rh	Pd	Ag	Cd	In	Sn	Sb	Te	I	Xe

Figure 1.3   Elements in organisms. The elements in hatched boxes in this (partial) periodic table occur in living organisms. Some are required only in trace amounts. By definition, carbon occurs in all organic compounds and hydrogen and oxygen occur in most. Nitrogen, sulphur and phosphorus also occur in some important cellular compounds.

Some of these elements exist mainly as simple *inorganic* ions dissolved in the water that makes up 80–90% of most organisms. Sodium (Na^+), potassium (K^+) and chloride ions (Cl^-) are examples. Others occur as insoluble inorganic compounds, such as calcium carbonate ($CaCO_3$) in bones and shells, or silica (SiO_2) in the sharp tips of plant roots. Note that carbon dioxide and both carbonate and bicarbonate ions are regarded as inorganic sources of carbon. Several others, especially the elements carbon, hydrogen, oxygen, nitrogen and sulphur, are present in several thousand different *organic* compounds found across the range of organisms that inhabit the biosphere (i.e. the Earth's surface, the sea and the air).

Compare, however, this relatively small number of biological compounds (numbering just a few thousand) with the millions of different species that currently exist. Clearly then, the same few chemicals occur in most organisms. And, just as the number of molecules is limited, so also is the range of chemical reactions that they undergo. Although the biochemistry of plants does differ from that of animals (for example, in photosynthesis), most of their biochemical make-up is identical. This characteristic, of *limited* differences in biochemical structure and function is what you would expect if present day life arose from common ancestors, with modification over time through the process of evolution. The underlying unity of biochemistry confirms this.

> *Give examples illustrating the extent to which different species have similar biochemical processes, and the extent to which they differ.*

Compounds	Comments
Inorganic compounds	
Ions in solution in water: e.g. H^+, Na^+, K^+, Ca^{2+}, Mg^{2+}, OH^-, Cl^-, PO_4^{3-}, HCO_3^-	Roles of ions are very varied, e.g. K^+ in nerve impulse, Ca^{2+} in muscle contraction, Mg^{2+} as an enzyme activator
Carbon dioxide	
Insoluble compounds, e.g. in teeth and bone	Bone is about 30% collagen (a protein) and 70% bone salts, especially insoluble calcium phosphate
Organic compounds	
Biological polymers (biopolymers), especially polysaccharides, proteins and nucleic acids (DNA and RNA)	Most roles of polysaccharides are concerned with structure, e.g. the cellulose of plant cell walls, or with food storage, e.g. starch Proteins – see text DNA – see text RNA – makes proteins
Lipids. This group includes triglycerides (simple fats) and phospholipids. It also includes the fatty acids from fat	Simple fats are food storage compounds, e.g. found in adipose tissue in animals, and oil in plant seeds Phospholipids are found in cell membranes
Monomers that make up the polymers, e.g. monosaccharides, amino acids, nucleotides	Each biopolymer consists of many monomers
Intermediary metabolites (the small compounds of biochemistry), e.g. pyruvic acid, acetyl CoA	When one substance is changed into another, the conversion involves several intermediate compounds (intermediary metabolites)
Coenzymes. These are small organic molecules that work with enzymes, e.g. NAD^+	

Table 1.1 Main characteristics of compounds found in organisms.

However, returning to the question of inorganic and organic compounds, what other things would you mention if asked by some visiting 'alien from outer space' to say more about the chemistry of life? One response might well focus on *water*, hydrogen oxide (H_2O). Life almost certainly originated in water. Most organisms are composed mainly of water and it has special properties that make it an excellent medium for chemical reactions. Alternatively, focusing on the organic compounds, you could have said more about the element *carbon*. This element, the sixth in the periodic table (atomic number 6), has the power to form stable covalent bonds with oxygen, hydrogen, nitrogen and sulphur, but above all with itself, thus making possible the huge number of organic compounds. Table 1.1 lists the main categories of these compounds that are found in organisms. More will be said about these compounds in Chapter 2. Two types of compound listed in Table 1.1 are especially significant and have crucial roles in *all* organisms. These are the nucleic acids and proteins.

■ Nucleic acids

To gain some idea about nucleic acids, look at Fig. 1.4. This shows the 23 pairs of chromosomes that carry the entire genetic message of the human zygote, i.e. the fertilised egg.

In these chromosomes are a large number of molecules of DNA linked to various kinds of protein molecule. The DNA molecules, each one itself of enormous length, are the actual *genetic chemicals*. The 3.4 picograms of DNA that you inherited from your mother's ovum, together with the same mass you gained from the sperm that fertilised it, have made you the particular size, shape and colour of human that you are, instead of a warthog or an oak tree. If you multiply the 6.8 picograms in the zygote by 5 000 000 000, i.e. the number of humans alive now, you get about 0.03 g. So, less than a pin head's mass of DNA codes for the whole human race! *How* the structure of this almost incredible chemical enables it to encode the message 'make a cat' or 'make an *E. coli*', 'make a white human male' or 'make a black human female', and *how* that message is turned into reality, is the subject of Chapter 4.

Describe the structure of DNA and explain how its structure enables it to function as the genetic substance in almost all organisms.

(a) Cells are taken from living tissue (or from amniotic fluid surrounding a foetus). These isolated cells are mounted, stained and fixed.

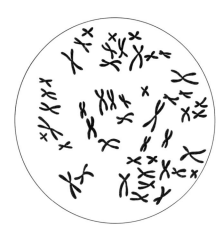

(b) A photograph is taken of the stained chromosomes from one cell — as seen under a microscope.

(c) The photographic image of each chromosome is cut out and paired up. Each pair is arranged in descending order of size. The presence of two X chromosomes indicates a female. The presence of three chromosomes 21 (as seen above) shows trisomy-21, Downs syndrome.

Figure 1.4 Karyotype of a human female with Downs syndrome. Note that (b) and (c) are drawings prepared from photographs. There are other kinds of chromosome disorder, e.g. trisomy-11, three chromosomes 11, a very rare and fatal condition.

■ Proteins

But what of proteins? The very word was coined from the Greek *proteios* meaning 'primary' or 'of first rank'. In every one of us there are many thousands of different proteins, each having its own essential role. Proteins serve as hormones and enzymes and have other roles in muscles and cell membranes, in the immune system, in skin, feathers, hair and wool, etc. The list is seemingly endless. The detail of this is developed in Chapter 2, but for now the key point is to note how totally essential proteins are.

Even more important is the link between the DNA mentioned earlier and these proteins. It is through proteins that DNA makes its message real. If one of your chromosomes carries a *gene* which codes for 'brown eyes', the DNA of that gene makes a particular *protein* that brings about the biochemical reactions necessary to make the *brown pigment* of the eye. In general terms, this relationship may be expressed thus: every reaction in your body is brought about by its own, unique protein, and every different protein is coded for and made under the direction of its own unique DNA molecule. Much of Chapter 2 and all of Chapter 3 concerns the structure and function of proteins of various kinds, and Chapter 4 explains how the genetic coding system works.

> *Describe the structure of proteins. How does the structure of any given protein determine its biological properties?*

> *In addition to the nucleic acids and proteins, what other kinds of biopolymer are important? Discuss their structure and function.*

■ THE INTERNAL STRUCTURE OF ORGANISMS

Earliest life (3.5 billion years ago, remember?) was formed in the warm primordial soup of organic compounds in the ancient seas. Yet, if you stick a pin in a modern day elephant you do not get a gush of that soup! There is much more to the structure of organisms than mere chemicals. In fact, biologists use several *levels of organisation* to describe any organism.

At the highest level (continuing with elephants as our example) there is the elephant herd and its re-

lationship with the ecosystem of which it is a part. Then there is the single, entire elephant, and below that, the organ systems and organs of which they are composed. The elephant's digestive system is one example of an organ system. And so on down, through organs, tissues, cells, sub-cellular organelles, membranes and solutions and finally molecules. Biochemists are concerned with all these levels of organisation.

However, it is at the level of cell structure and below that biochemists are most interested. Before going into detail about cells it is important to realise that there are two main types of cell. Bacteria are unicellular organisms and have, in comparative terms, a very simple cellular structure. The single cell that constitutes the whole organism has no true nucleus and no distinct membrane-bound subcellular organelles. The absence of a nucleus gives the whole bacterial kingdom its descriptive term, i.e. the *prokaryotes*. The word prokaryote is Greek in origin and literally means 'before a proper nucleus' and hints at the idea that bacteria evolved before other life forms. *All* other organisms in the other four kingdoms have a true nucleus. They also have a range of completely membrane-enclosed organelles, of which the mitochondria, and chloroplasts are examples. Cells of this type are described as eukaryotic and the organisms possessing them as *eukaryotes* (eukaryote means 'true nucleus'). Thus all plants, animals, protoctists and fungi are eukaryotes.

Figure 1.5 overleaf shows in diagrammatic form the generalised subcellular structure of a bacterium, a plant cell and an animal cell. You will see in later chapters that *it is very important indeed to know about the chemical make-up of these sub-cellular structures, what they do biochemically, and how their function contributes to the life of the organism as a whole.*

Table 1.2 overleaf summarises the main differences between prokaryotes and eukaryotes.

> *Describe the components of eukaryotic cells. What biochemical processes occur within them? How do these processes contribute to the life of the organism as a whole?*

> *In what ways do the structures and, hence, the biochemical functions of plant and animal cells differ?*

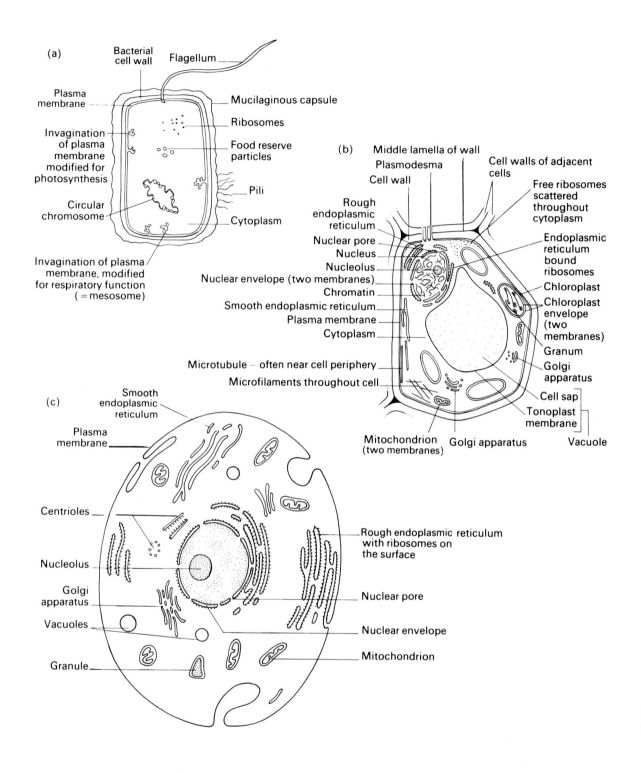

Figure 1.5 The generalised structure of a) a bacterium, b) a plant cell and c) an animal cell. The component parts are labelled but relative sizes are not to scale. Most plant cells are larger than animal cells, and bacterial cells are much smaller than either. The functions of the cell organelles are described later in the text.

6

Prokaryotes	Eukaryotes
A: organism type: bacteria and blue-green algae	*A*: animals, plants, fungi and protoctists
B: form of organisms: mostly unicellular; a few are linear filaments of unicells	*B*: some are unicellular but most are multicellular with a complex 'division of labour' between different types of cells
C: cell size: usually about 1–10 μm long	*C*: usually about 10–100 μm long
D: location of genetic material: DNA occurs as a single circular chromosome which is not membrane-bound	*D*: chromosomes are located inside an envelope formed from two membranes (i.e. a nucleus). There are pores in the envelope
E: other structures in cytoplasm: some membranes may exist but never forming an envelope	*E*: all contain mitochondria: others depending on species, contain chloroplasts, liposomes, golgi body, endoplasmic reticulum (see Fig. 1.5)
F: ribosomes: these small particles are involved in protein synthesis. In prokaryotes ribosomes are relatively small (described as '70S' ribosomes)	*F*: in eukaryotes, ribosomes are relatively large (described as '80S' ribosomes)
G: metabolism: some are autotrophs and some are heterotrophs. Of the heterotrophs, some are aerobic and some are anaerobic	*G*: some protoctists and all plants are autotrophs. Of the heterotrophs most are aerobic. Some can be anaerobic

Table 1.2 Comparison of prokaryotes and eukaryotes. Many of the terms are described later in the text. Features D and E are used to *define* the term prokaryote and eukaryote.

■ BLUEPRINTS, MATERIALS AND ENERGY

In this chapter so far, you have been given, from a biochemist's standpoint, a view of the origin and diversity of life. You have been given a brief description of the range of chemicals involved. You now know that cells have internal structures, and that these structures are involved in a number of biochemical processes. But what of the *nature* of these processes?

Look around your room at home, at your cat asleep on the bed, a potted plant on the shelf, or yourself in a mirror. All organisms (those that sexually reproduce, that is), begin life as a zygote formed by the fusion of male and female gametes.

Before you read on, look at Fig. 1.6 overleaf and, based on what you read in the figure caption, do some brainstorming. What does a builder need to build a house? What is required to progress from a zygote to an adult? The answers, in the analogy of the house and in the biological reality of plants and animals, are the following:

● **You need a blueprint**. Without a blueprint, the bricks might have formed a bus-shelter instead of a house: your cat might have sired a giraffe instead of a kitten. The genetic code, written in a sequence of nucleotides in the structure of DNA, is the true blueprint.

● **You need materials**. No bricks, no house! In the same way, unless you provide your cat with his Whiskas or Kattomeat, he will have no organic compounds with which to build cells and grow. Even the adult cat needs materials for new cell growth because all adults are in a state of perpetual turnover. In humans for example, half of the proteins of the liver are replaced every ten days. Chemically, few of the molecules that form you today formed the you of a year ago! Thus, you, the cat and all animals eat organic material. Organisms that obtain their organic carbon in this way are termed ***heterotrophs***.

---

heterotrophs   heterotrophs are organisms dependant on food from other living or dead organisms, i.e. they are unable to produce their own food from simple substances. Examples include all animals, fungi and some bacteria.

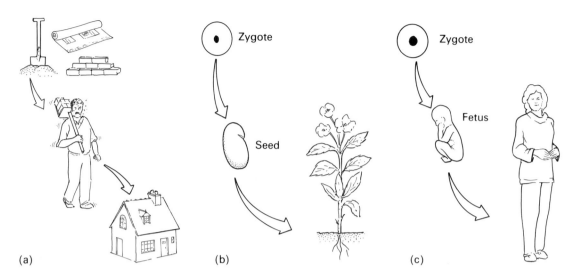

Figure 1.6 Growth. Look at Fig. 1.6(a). Decide, from common sense, what three fundamental requirements must be met if the house is to be built. Apply the result of your thinking to plant and human growth in (b) and (c).

Plants are different. They need organic compounds just as much as animals do. They also need to build cells out of proteins, nucleic acids, polysaccharides, fats and so on. But, they do not take in organic compounds. Instead, their source of carbon is carbon dioxide from the atmosphere and from it, using the process of photosynthesis, they form all the organic compounds they need. Organisms that obtain their organic carbon by making it themselves from carbon dioxide are termed **autotrophs**.

● **You need energy**. To create the organised structure of a house where previously there was the disorder of heaps of bricks, requires energy. Similarly, an adequate supply of biologically useful energy is required to make cellular molecules from their components and to arrange those molecules in an ordered way.

In fact, all heterotrophs obtain their biologically useful energy by breaking down some of the organic compounds that they consume. The set of 'breaking down' reactions within an organism is called its **catabolism**. Mostly these catabolic processes are oxidations. Autrophs behave in a strikingly similar way to heterotrophs in that they obtain biologically useful energy by oxidising organic compounds. Thus, oxidative catabolism is as important to a fern as it is to a cat. The only difference is that autotrophs make the oxidisable fuel themselves from carbon dioxide and water, using solar energy.

What are autotrophs and heterotrophs? Describe biochemical differences between them. How do these biochemical characteristics relate to food-chains, production ecology and the carbon, nitrogen, sulphur and phosphorus cycles in ecology?

Growth depends on the production of new cells. Describe the biochemical principles that underlie the process of growth.

autotrophs all photosynthetic organisms are autotrophs and are called *photoautotrophs*. Examples include plants, some protoctists and some bacteria, e.g. green and blue-green bacteria. Some non-photosynthetic bacteria convert carbon dioxide to organic compounds using energy from inorganic reactions instead of light energy. These organisms are called *chemoautotrophs*.

catabolism *metabolism* is the term applied to all biochemical processes within organisms. Catabolism involves the breaking down of substances with an accompanying release of energy. The converse, anabolism, is the building up of large molecules from smaller precursors and requires an input of energy. Another word for anabolism is biosynthesis. The word anabolic has entered everyday language in the context of anabolic steroids. These are much disapproved of body-building hormones taken illegally by some athletes.

■ BIOENERGETICS

As we have seen, the creation of cells with their complex and highly organised systems requires an input of energy. The concept of 'converting energy from one form to another' is very important in biology, and needs a proper introduction. Underlying all questions of bioenergetics (i.e. energy conversions in biology) is the *Law of conservation of energy*. This states that energy cannot be created or destroyed, though it can be converted from one form into another. Remembering that energy has the same units as 'work' and is measured in joules, it is possible to get a very good idea of energy conservation, hence of bioenergetics, by doing some simple brainstorming.

Consider an energetic baby. In what form does a baby receive energy? Into what forms is that energy converted? The *chemical potential energy* of the organic compounds in a baby's food is transformed into several forms of energy. Some of the food energy is used to make new chemical compounds in the baby's body. Thus, some energy is used in *biosynthesis*. Some of the energy is transformed by the baby into *kinetic energy* by moving muscles (e.g. the kicking of arms and legs). Some energy is expended in a rather invisible but nevertheless essential way, doing work through *active transport*. This involves moving substances across a membrane against a concentration gradient (the production of urine by the baby's kidneys, for example).

Apart from fireflies and glow-worms which produce light energy, there is only one other kind of energy that has not so far been mentioned, that is heat energy. All biological energy transformations are inefficient, in the same way that a car is inefficient at transforming the chemical energy of petrol into kinetic energy of motion. With organisms, as with cars, heat is an inevitable side-product. Such heat production can be both a bonus and a problem to the organism.

Energy transformation also occurs in plants. In bioenergetic terms, solar energy is captured by plants (and photosynthetic bacteria) by the process of photosynthesis. The organic compounds which are made serve the organism in exactly the same way as food molecules serve us. The organic compounds are catabolised by the plant cells and some of the chemical potential energy thus released is used to make new organic compounds. Some of the energy is used in active transport, for example when nitrate ions are absorbed from a weak solution in soil into a stronger solution in the cytoplasm of the plant's root hair cells. Inevitably also, a small amount of heat is produced as a result of inefficient energy conversion.

It is clear from the above that the following important questions need to be answered.

- *How* is the food obtained by organisms catabolised in such a way that its chemical potential energy is made available?
- *How* is that released energy conveyed to the energy-requiring processes such as leaf growth, muscle contraction, bacterial movement, etc?
- *How* is heat produced during these transformations?
- *How* are new organic compounds formed (biosynthesised) inside the organism?

Though some of these difficult questions are answered in more detail in later chapters, there is one feature that appears in every answer and that is the role of a substance called **adenosine triphosphate (ATP)**. ATP is almost certainly present in every living organism except viruses. In all cases it acts as the *energy currency* of the cell. What do we mean by this?

Consider a mechanical system such as an old fashioned steam engine. The law of energy conservation applies here as everywhere. The chemical potential energy of the coal is released by breaking it down to carbon dioxide and water. This release is achieved by oxidation in the form of a fire beneath the engine's boiler. The result is lots of *heat* that boils the water, produces the steam, powers the pistons and so is transformed into kinetic energy. Here, the energy currency is the heat itself. This does not happen **in vivo**. The release of heat on that scale and in that way would, literally, fry an organism. Instead

---

ATP adenosine triphosphate consists of adenine and ribose molecules and a triphosphate group.

in vivo *in vivo* means 'within the living organism'. The converse, *in vitro*, means outside the living organism. *In vitro* literally means 'in glass'.

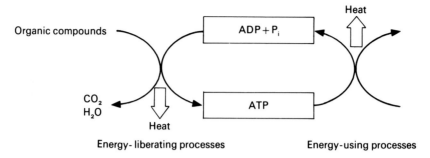

Figure 1.7 The role of ATP. ATP is often described as the 'energy' currency of cells. There are only about 5 g of ATP in an entire human body — yet the entire energy flow (from the oxidation of three square meals a day!) passes through this ATP making and using process. This ADP/ATP cycle happens, in molecular terms, millions of times each day!

the energy released by catabolism, i.e. the energy-liberating (*exergonic*) processes, is temporarily captured by the synthesis of adenosine triphosphate from adenosine diphosphate (ADP) and inorganic phosphate (P_i). To appreciate this transfer of energy more fully, look at Fig. 1.7.

You can regard ATP as a 'wound-up chemical clockwork motor' and ADP as a 'run-down chemical clockwork motor'. The inorganic phosphate (P_i) provides the difference between the **di**phosphate and the **tri**phosphate. The energy-using (*endergonic*) processes, you will remember from the example of the baby, are biosynthesis, muscular work, and work through active transport. The actual amount of energy captured or made available by the interconversion of ADP and ATP has been measured and is in the order of 40 kJ per mole. This value is important in later chapters when the catabolism of glucose is discussed in detail.

The energy-liberating processes of catabolism wind up the 'motor', making ATP from ADP and P_i. The energy-using processes are driven by the ATP 'motor' which is consequently converted back to ADP and P_i. The ATP/ADP interconversion is, therefore, the essential link between the exergonic and endergonic activities of the organism. As shown in Fig. 1.7, the inefficiency of the link between exergonic processes and ATP production and between endergonic processes and ATP utilisation means that there is substantial heat production at both stages. This leakage of heat is, however, important in maintaining body temperature.

The story of how ATP is made by photosynthesis in plants and by respiration in *both* plants and animals is a major topic in biochemistry and is dealt with in later chapters. For now, the basic ideas of energy transformation, exergonic and endergonic processes and the linking role of ATP form an excellent start. The next set of boxed 'organiser' questions will be answerable after completing the later chapters.

How do green plants make ATP from ADP and P_i using solar energy? How do they then use the chemical potential energy in that ATP to convert carbon dioxide and water into carbohydrates? How are plant chloroplasts involved in that process?

How do green plants oxidatively catabolise the organic compounds they make by photosynthesis? How is ATP made from ADP and P_i as a consequence? How do heterotrophs — that obtain their organic compounds directly or indirectly from plants — oxidatively catabolise such compounds? How is ATP made from ADP and P_i as a consequence? In both animals and plants, how are mitochondria involved in this ATP-making process?

Now that this general introduction to biochemistry is complete, you should be ready to take a closer and more detailed look. We begin in the next chapter by focusing on the most fundamental level of cellular organisation, that of the molecules themselves.

THE CHEMICALS OF LIFE

■ INTRODUCTION

As we have seen in Chapter 1, organisms are incredibly complicated, and usually very different from one another. All of them, though, are made up of the same types of biochemicals, from the simplest bacterium to the most complex mammal. The biochemicals that are present will determine the nature of the organism – what it can or can't do, what it can or can't make, and what it does or doesn't look like.

In order to understand how a biochemical carries out a particular function in an organism, we have to look at the properties of the molecule. As the molecule gets its properties from its structure, it's right down at this structural level that we must look if we are to understand the processes of life. What is it, for example, that makes cellulose such a suitable molecule for plant cell walls, whilst cell membranes contain so much lipid? You will find that the relationship between biochemical structure and biological function comes up time and again in this and following chapters. We will begin, however, by focusing on the molecule that more than any other makes the chemistry of life possible. And that is the water molecule.

■ WATER

Scientists have concluded that there is little chance of life on Mars or on any of the other planets in the solar system because they don't have any liquid water. If we look at our own planet, Earth, over two-thirds of it is covered with water, and the evidence is that life itself began in the oceans (the 'primordial soup' of Chapter 1). Living organisms themselves are about 80% water by mass, and must retain this level to survive.

So, what is so special about water? To answer this

Figure 2.1   The water molecule. Note slight charges – hence water is a **polar** molecule.

question fully we need to look at the structure of water, see what are the properties of water and find out what water can do. Compared with other molecules, a water molecule is very small, two atoms of hydrogen joined by covalent bonds to one atom of oxygen (i.e. H_2O). Covalent bonds are formed by sharing electrons in the outer orbits of the atoms. In the case of water, however, the large number of protons in the oxygen nucleus have a stronger attraction for these shared electrons than the tiny hydrogen nucleus does. This pulls the electrons slightly closer to the oxygen atom and away from the hydrogen, so that the oxygen develops a very small negative charge and the hydrogens a small positive charge, i.e. the molecule is slightly *polar* (see Fig. 2.1).

When water molecules are close together, the positively charged hydrogen of one water molecule is attracted to the negatively charged oxygen of another molecule to form a *hydrogen bond*. These hydrogen bonds are very weak and are continually being broken and remade. However, the sheer number formed means that the total force keeping the water molecules together is considerable. Each water molecule tends to form four hydrogen bonds, and it is this capacity for hydrogen bond formation that causes water to be a liquid at room temperature rather than a gas. This is but one of the set of properties that make it possible for water to fulfil its role as the 'medium' in which the reactions of life occur (see Fig. 2.2).

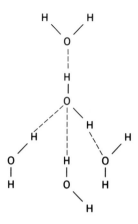

Figure 2.2 Hydrogen bonding in water. Note that each water molecule tends to form four hydrogen bonds.

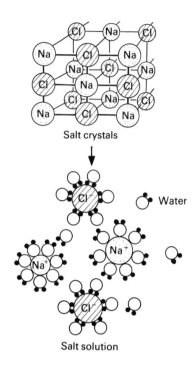

Salt crystals

Water

Salt solution

Figure 2.3 Salt dissolving in water.

■ PROPERTIES OF WATER

The properties of water allow it to behave in a number of ways:

● as a solvent;
● as a reactant;
● as a molecule with cohesive properties;
● as a temperature stabiliser;
● as an environment.

■ Water as a solvent

Because of its polarity and ability to hydrogen bond, water is a superb solvent, capable of dissolving more substances than virtually any other liquid. Most substances that are ionic or polar will dissolve in water. For example, common salt (sodium chloride, NaCl) is made up of a positive sodium ion strongly attracted to a negative chloride ion. Usually it would take a large amount of energy to break this ionic bond, but when salt is put into water the negative oxygen atoms cluster around the sodium ion (Na^+) and the positive hydrogen atoms are attracted to the chloride ion (Cl^-). The attraction between the sodium and chloride is weakened as a result and the ions separate. As you can see from Fig. 2.3, once dissolved the polar water molecules cluster round the sodium and chloride ions keeping them fully separated.

Many biological molecules are covalent rather than ionic. However, these too will dissolve in water *provided they have polar groups within them*. Sucrose is a sugar that plants transport around their systems. It is also the ordinary table sugar that you put in your tea or coffee. When you stir in a spoonful of this sucrose, the polar hydroxyl groups (—OH) in its structure form hydrogen bonds with the water, so separating the sucrose molecules from each other.

The importance of this property of water to living systems is obvious, as most biochemical reactions take place in solution. The advantages of having such a powerful solvent available are immense. It is therefore not surprising that the cytoplasm of cells is about 90% water.

■ Water as a reactant

Water takes part in a considerable number of biochemical reactions, such as the *hydrolysis* ('hydro' means water, 'lysis' means splitting) of large molecules into smaller ones. As you will see later, water is a key molecule in the most important synthesis reaction in any ecosystem, i.e. photosynthesis.

■ Water as a molecule with cohesive properties

Because of the hydrogen bonds, the water molecules have considerable *cohesive* properties. This cohesion allows plants to pull water up from the roots to the leaves. It also means that at an air-water interface such as that found at the surface of a pond, the water molecules at the top will be tightly held to each other and to the water molecules below them to form an elastic film. This effect is called surface tension, and is what enables insects such as pond skaters to move across the water surface without sinking.

■ Water as a temperature stabiliser

Water has a very high *specific heat capacity*. The result of this is that it takes a lot of heat to raise the temperature of water, but once it is warm it cools down slowly. This means that organisms that live on land don't need to be hyperactive the moment the sun comes out due to the extra heat rapidly increasing their metabolic rate, nor do they need to slow down the moment the sun goes behind a cloud.

Because of the large number of hydrogen bonds holding water molecules together, it takes a considerable amount of heat to separate these molecules and turn the liquid into a vapour (i.e. water has a high *latent heat of vaporisation*). Many terrestrial animals utilise this property by using their body heat to evaporate water from their surfaces, with the result that they are cooled down. Sweating and panting are based on this principle.

As water cools, it becomes more and more dense, the hydrogen bonds between the molecules take on a more ordered lattice arrangement and, as Fig. 2.4 shows, the water turns into ice. The molecules are less densely packed together in this crystalline structure, with the result that ice floats.

This property of ice is vital to aquatic organisms, as in cold weather the ice forms an insulating layer on the top of ponds, canals, etc. This means that the water beneath the ice stays in the liquid state and life is able to continue.

---

cohesion the attraction of 'like' particles.

specific heat capacity this is the amount of energy needed to raise 1 kg of substance by 1 K. Water has a specific heat capacity of $4184\,J\,kg^{-1}K^{-1}$.

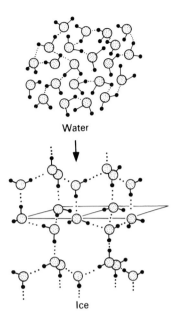

Water

Ice

Figure 2.4 Water turning to ice. The closely packed molecules take on a more ordered arrangement, with large spaces between them. Ice is less dense than water, and is therefore lighter.

■ Water as an environment

Because water covers most of the Earth's surface, it is likely that it would have been colonised by some of the earliest forms of life. When the properties of water are looked at more closely, though, several advantages of living in this medium become apparent and it is not surprising that life began here.

1. Due to its high specific heat capacity, large bodies of water will remain at an almost constant temperature with only very gradual changes. This makes temperature regulation for organisms a far more straightforward process.

2. Because water molecules 'stick' to each other by hydrogen bonding, they provide considerable support for fish, plants, etc. This means that these organisms then don't need to devote so much in the way of resources to providing supporting tissue such as bone or wood. A land animal the size of the blue whale would be impossible as it would collapse under its own weight.

3. Water allows light to pass through it (to a depth of 200 metres in the case of blue light), as long as there are no particles suspended in it. This property is vital to water plants.

4. Water helps to remove soluble waste products from the body to the environment.

CARBOHYDRATES

All carbohydrates contain the elements carbon (C), hydrogen (H) and oxygen (O), with the latter two elements being present in a 2:1 ratio. The general formula of a carbohydrate can thus be generally written as $C_x(H_2O)_y$. For example, the formula for sucrose is $C_{12}H_{22}O_{11}$.

In nature, there are many carbohydrates with a range of structures and very important functions. From general knowledge, many people would recognise ordinary table sugar (sucrose) as a carbohydrate. Because of people's weight problems, most will know that the starch in potatoes, bread and rice is also a carbohydrate. But fewer will know that the brown exoskeleton of insects is also a carbohydrate; its name is chitin. Heparin, the compound that stops blood clotting and is given to some heart patients, is yet another carbohydrate. So is the cellulose of wood, the sweetness in Lucozade, and the jelly-like coating on seaweeds! Figure 2.5 shows the way in which carbohydrates can be classified and the compounds named are those that will be discussed most frequently.

On the right hand side of Fig. 2.5 are found all the polysaccharides. As the name 'poly' suggests, a polysaccharide molecule is made up of *many* monosaccharides joined together. These monosaccharides are found on the far left of the Figure along with disaccharides, i.e. molecules of two monosaccharides joined together. There are a number of different monosaccharides in biology but the commonest of these is glucose. Fortunately, all the polysaccharides you need to know about (except chitin) are simply polymers of glucose! Let's look in more detail at the sugars (the names of which end in -ose).

Monosaccharides

Monosaccharides are simple sugars, broadly classified according to the number of carbon atoms in the molecule. Thus, we get the trioses (3 carbons), tetroses (4), pentoses, (5), hexoses (6), and so on.

Trioses

The trioses are the smallest of the monosaccharides. There are only two trioses, i.e. glyceraldehyde and dihydroxyacetone. These trioses contain an aldehyde group (—CHO) or a ketone group (—C=O). This is true for all monosaccharides, and gives them the ability to donate electrons to other molecules, i.e. they are *reducing* sugars. This property forms the basis of the standard test for them. If you look at Fig. 2.6, you'll see that although the sugars have the same formula, $C_3H_6O_3$, they have different structures, i.e. they are *structural isomers*.

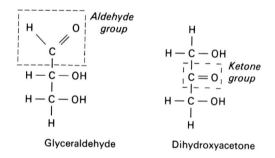

Figure 2.6 Structural isomers.

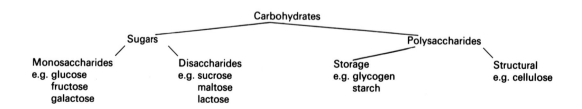

Figure 2.5 Classification of carbohydrates.

Test for reducing sugars

Make a solution of the substance to be tested and add Benedict's solution. Boil. If reducing sugars are present, they will reduce the copper ions in the Benedict's solution to form a precipitate. The colour of the precipitate gives an idea as to how much sugar is present, i.e. green (low sugar content), through to red-brown (high sugar content).

There is one other point to consider. In the trioses, and all other monosaccharides, there is at least one carbon atom attached to four different chemical groups. This is called an *asymmetric* carbon atom. Because of the way in which the bonds are directed, two arrangements of the asymmetric carbon atoms are possible which are mirror images of each other. These are called the D- and L-*optical isomers* (see Fig. 2.7).

It is interesting to note that only the D-isomers of sugars are found in most living systems. Nobody knows why. It has been suggested that the L-isomers of sugars should be made available as slimming aids. They are sweet and stimulate the taste buds but as they are not metabolised, they don't add to the calorie count. Can you think of problems in using this idea?

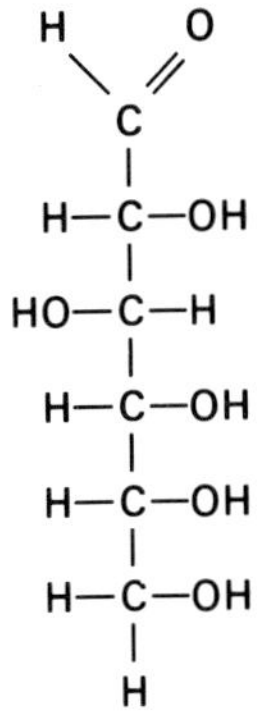

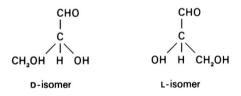

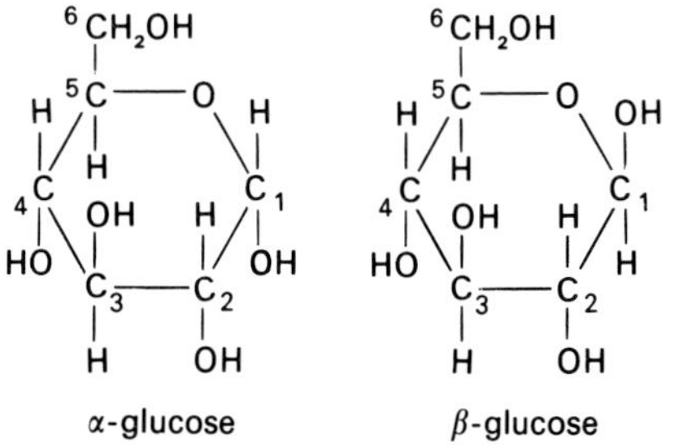

Figure 2.7 The two forms of glyceraldehyde. Imagine putting the D-isomer in front of a mirror – the reflection would be the L-isomer.

Pentoses

Of the pentoses, ribose and deoxyribose are of major interest. These are components of nucleotides, the building blocks of the nucleic acids, DNA and RNA. This will be covered in more detail in Chapter 4.

Hexoses

The hexoses all have the formula $C_6H_{12}O_6$. The chemical groups can be arranged in the molecule in a number of different ways and there are, therefore, a large number of isomers found in living systems, e.g. glucose, fructose and galactose.

Figure 2.8 Straight chain formula of glucose.

In solution, few straight chain molecules of hexoses exist. All molecules will take up a shape that requires the least amount of energy to maintain and in the case of the hexoses, this shape is a five or six-sided ring. This is shown in Fig. 2.9.

Figure 2.9 The numbering system exists because it is convenient to be able to refer to specific carbon atoms in the molecule. Carbon 1 of glucose is asymmetric. It has four groups, i.e. C, OH, O and CHOH attached, and so can exist in two forms, i.e. α and β.

■ Disaccharides

Disaccharides are very widespread in plants and form an important part of the diet of many heterotrophs. Sugar beet, sugar cane and in fact all plant tissues are rich in sucrose. Milk (which tastes slightly sweet) contains lactose. Partially broken down starch, e.g. the brown sticky 'malt' that can be bought in health shops, contains maltose. Sucrose, lactose and maltose are all disaccharides, i.e. molecules in which two monosaccharides are joined together. At this level, you will need to know something about each of these sugars, including a number of their properties.

As Fig. 2.10 shows, two monosaccharides can be linked together to form a disaccharide. This results in the removal of a molecule of water. Any reaction involving the removal of a water molecule is known as a *condensation* reaction. The bond formed between two monosaccharides is known as a *glycosidic* bond. If we look at maltose, the bond is formed between carbon 1 of one α-glucose and carbon 4 of another α-glucose and so it is referred to as a 1–4 glycosidic bond. The arrangement of the bond always takes its name from the conformation of the carbon 1 taking part in the reaction, hence the above is an α1–4 glycosidic bond. To break the glycosidic bond, a molecule of water is added and a *hydrolysis reaction* occurs.

Maltose (i.e. glucose-glucose) is often known as brewer's sugar. In the brewing process it is formed by breaking down the starch reserves in barley grains. The maltose is then itself broken down by the yeast to form alcohol.

Lactose (i.e. glucose-galactose) is the main sugar found in milk and so provides the major source of carbohydrates for young mammals. Some human babies are unable to process the galactose formed from the breakdown of lactose, and so the galactose builds up to toxic levels. This condition is called galactosaemia, and affected babies must avoid milk and be given carbohydrate in some other form.

Sucrose (i.e. glucose-fructose) is the sugar you use at home to sweeten food and drinks. However, unlike maltose and lactose, it is a non-reducing sugar. The reducing part of the glucose molecule is hidden in the bond. Sucrose can be detected by hydrolysing it first with hydrochloric acid to give glucose and fructose, and then using the Benedict test after the acid has been neutralised with an alkali. Figure 2.11 shows a molecule of lactose and a molecule of sucrose.

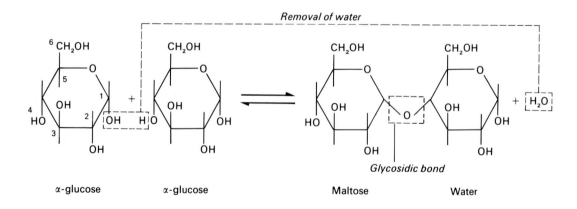

Figure 2.10 Production of maltose by formation of a 1-4 glycosidic bond. (In this and the following diagrams the hydrogen atoms are omitted for the sake of clarity.)

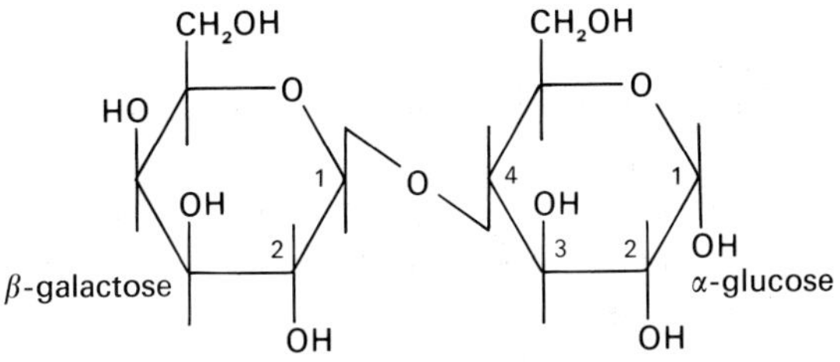

Lactose

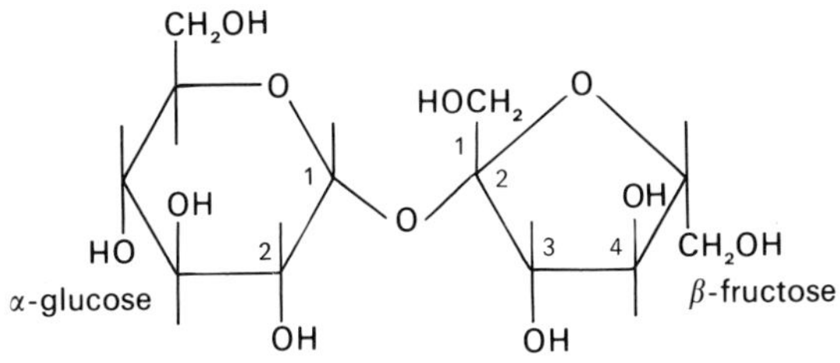

Sucrose

Figure 2.11 Note the $\beta 1-4$ bond in lactose and the $\alpha 1-2$ bond in sucrose.

■ Roles of monosaccharides and disaccharides

● When sugars are respired, the reactions yield a large amount of energy. This is a major function of monosaccharides and disaccharides in living systems, i.e. to provide a readily obtainable supply of energy.

● All monosaccharides and disaccharides are soluble due to their hydroxyl groups being able to interact with water. This property is vital if they are to take part in biochemical reactions. It also means that they are easily transported in multicellular organisms, usually in the form of glucose in animals and sucrose in plants.

● All monosaccharides and disaccharides are sweet. It is believed that their sweetness is due to the arrangement of hydroxyl groups with respect to each other, and so some sugars are sweeter than others. This may seem to be an unimportant property, but plants make use of it as a biological 'bribe'. Most animals like sweet-tasting substances, and are attracted to fruits which contain fructose, one of the

sweeter sugars. Seeds inside the fruit which are resistant to the animal's digestive juices are thus efficiently dispersed.

● Monosaccharides and disaccharides are crystalline. Plants such as sugar cane store high levels of carbohydrate in this form.

● Monosaccharides can be combined together to form disaccharides and polysaccharides.

■ Polysaccharides

In polysaccharides, the monosaccharide building blocks are linked together by glycosidic bonds to form **polymer** chains hundreds of units long. The monomer is usually glucose, and the resulting polysaccharides, although differing from each other in structure, all have one thing in common – they are so large as to be relatively insoluble. They can be broadly divided into two groups according to their function:

● storage polysaccharides;
● structural polysaccharides.

Storage polysaccharides

Any food storage molecule must provide a freely available source of the required substance without taking up too much space or upsetting the *osmotic balance* of the cell (i.e. the concentration of different solutes in solution). With regard to glucose storage, starch carries out this role in plants and glycogen carries out the same role in animals.

Starch is a polymer of α-glucose, and is found as large grains in plant storage tissue. Starch is made up of two different polysaccharides, *amylose* and *amylopectin*. Amylose makes up about 15–30% of the molecules are joined together by $\alpha 1-4$ glycosidic bonds so that amylose takes up a helix shape with six glucose units in every turn. By adopting a helix shape

---

polymer   a condensation polymer is one in which the constituent molecules (known as *monomers*) are joined together, with the elimination of water. When one of these polymers reacts with water, the converse happens and the polymer is hydrolysed back to its constituent monomers. Digestion is an example of this hydrolysis.

the glucose chain takes up much less space (see Fig. 2.12).

When an 'iodine solution' is added to starch the iodine molecules pack very neatly inside the helix to give the classic test for starch, i.e. a blue-black colour that is impossible to miss.

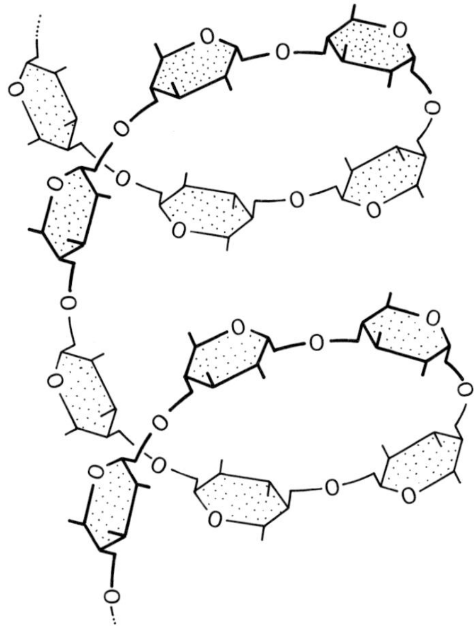

Amylopectin makes up the bulk of the starch grain and is wrapped around the amylose. The glucose molecules are joined together by $\alpha1-4$ bonds, but unlike amylose the glucose chain has branches coming off it. At about every twentieth glucose in the chain, an $\alpha1-6$ bond is formed with another glucose molecule and a side chain develops. This feature fulfils another requirement of a food storage molecule, i.e. ready availability. With all these 'loose ends', the amylopectin chain allows a number of enzyme molecules to act on it at any one time so it can easily be added to or broken down.

Glycogen is found in animal cells where glucose needs to be readily available in large amounts. These cells include skeletal muscle, where the energy demand can rise very suddenly with exercise and the liver, the organ responsible for regulating the blood glucose level. Glycogen is present in the form of small granules in the cytoplasm.

Because glycogen has much the same function as starch, it has a similar structure to amylopectin. However, the glycogen molecule is more heavily branched, with side chains coming off at about every twelfth glucose residue. This is possibly due to an animal's need for a more rapid mobilisation of its glucose reserves.

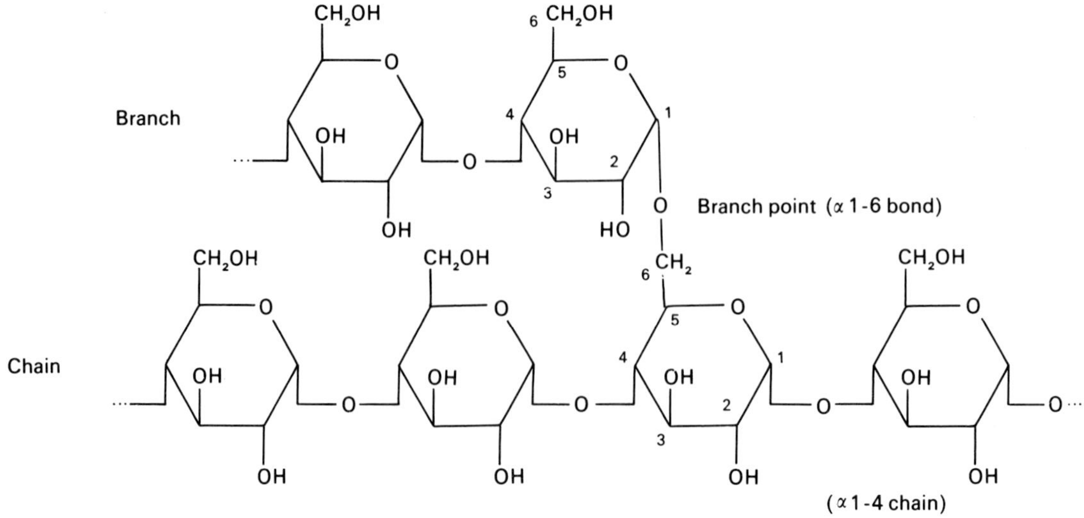

Figure 2.12 Part of an amylose molecule.

Figure 2.13 Shape of amylopectin.

18

As both starch and glycogen are relatively insoluble, they have little effect on the osmotic potential of the cell. If the amount of glucose present in the glycogen molecule were dissolved in the cytoplasm (if this amount could be dissolved!), it would certainly result in a rapid influx of water and cause the cell to burst. Also, if too much glucose was available (i.e. in solution) it would probably cause a lot of the cell reactions to happen at an undesirably high rate. In the form of a polysaccharide, the glucose is unavailable for use until it is released by an enzyme.

Structural polysaccharides

Without doubt, the most important member of this group is the polysaccharide that makes up every plant cell wall, i.e. *cellulose*. Cellulose, like amylose is a long, unbranched polymer of glucose, but in this case the glucose is a β-glucose. The result of changing from the α-isomer to a β-isomer is to give a zigzag ribbon-like molecule with the glucose rings lying in the plane of the ribbon and the —OH groups projecting from the sides. Hydrogen bonding occurs on a large scale between adjacent cellulose chains, packing them tightly together to form structures called microfibrils and giving considerable structural strength (see Fig. 2.14). Also present in the cell wall material are other polysaccharides such as pectins (the gelling agent in jam, incidentally), and hemicelluloses. How these are associated with the cellulose is not certain. However, it seems that they serve to cement the microfibrils together, adding further to the strength of the cell wall.

When another polymer called *lignin* is deposited in the plant cell wall, the strength and rigidity of the wall is increased enormously. This lignin deposition occurs when the plant-supporting tissue (sclerenchyma) is laid down. The cell wall is also effectively waterproofed by this process, and so lignin is also found in the cells of the water-conducting tissue (xylem) which forms the wood of the plant.

Animals do not usually make use of structural polysaccharides. One exception is *chitin*, the substance that makes up the exoskeleton of arthropods such as insects and crustaceans.

---

*Test for cellulose**

Add Schultz' solution (chlor-zinc-iodide) to the plant material and the cellulose will stain purple.

*Test for lignified cellulose**

Add acidified phloroglucinol to the plant material and a red colour results if lignin is present.

* *These tests can be done on thin sections of plant material.*

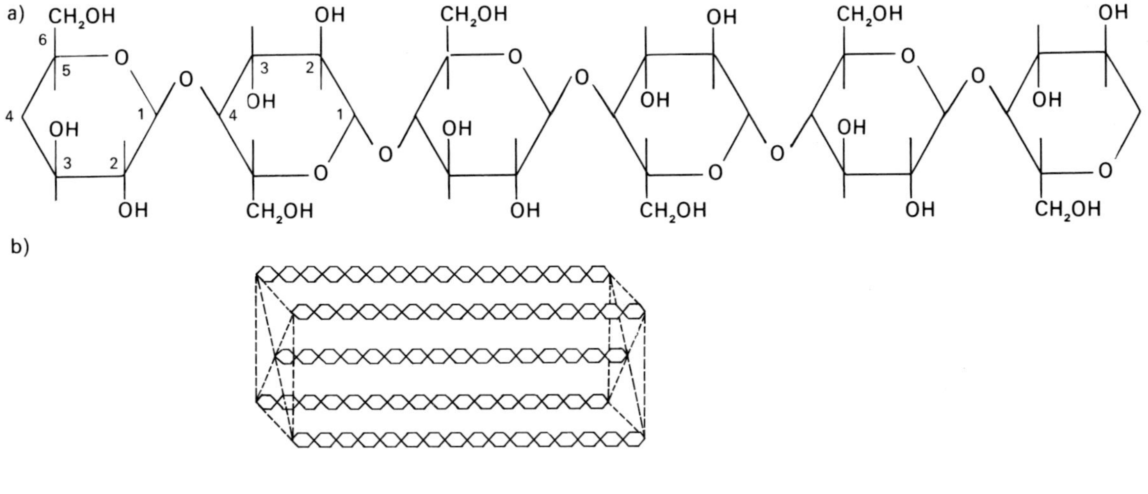

Figure 2.14   (a) Cellulose. Note that the glucose molecules are joined by β 1—4 bonds. (b) The chains of cellulose hydrogen bond to each other in a lattice-like arrangement to form a microfibril.

■ LIPIDS

Most people, unfamiliar with the term 'lipid', would be perfectly at home with the words 'fat' and 'oil'. Lipids are, in fact, a very mixed group of biological compounds that contain fats, oils, waxes (such as beeswax and that produced in the outer ear), fat-like compounds containing phosphorus (the phospholipids), and other compounds such as cholesterol and other steroids, long chain fatty acids, and so on. Taken as a whole, the only thing that is common to this group of compounds is that they are all fairly insoluble in water and quite soluble in various organic solvents such as petroleum, ether and chloroform.

Lipids are *vital* in the structure and function of all organisms, e.g. as a dietary source of energy for heterotrophs, as a food-store in the cells of animals, plants and bacteria, as components of cell membranes, and as insulators against heat, physical shock and electricity. They have many specialised functions too, e.g. the combs in beehives, the waxy cuticles that waterproof leaves, steroids, sex hormones and growth hormones. So, what is the chemistry of this diverse group?

Lipids, like the carbohydrates, contain carbon, hydrogen and oxygen, but the hydrogen and oxygen are not present in a 2:1 ratio. Among the lipids we find the oils (which are liquid at room temperature), fats and waxes (which are solid at room temperature), and the steroids.

> *Test for lipids*
>
> *Grind up the substance to be tested in water. Add a few drops of Sudan III solution and shake. If lipid is present, it rises to the surface and takes up the red stain. Water remains uncoloured.*

■ Structure

The fats and oils (often called simple lipids) are made up of a molecule of *glycerol* joined to three *fatty acids*. Glycerol is a small 3-carbon chemical obtained from glyceraldehyde (see page 14).

A fatty acid is composed of a long chain of carbon atoms combined with hydrogen. At the end of the chain is the acid group (—COOH, i.e. a carboxyl group). The fatty acid chain can have anything between 4 and 28 carbon atoms (see Table 2.1). It is worth looking at fatty acid chain structure in more detail, as it is these molecules which give the lipid its properties.

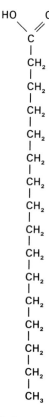

Figure 2.15 Palmitic acid ($C_{15}H_{31}COOH$).

Name	Formula	No. of carbon atoms	No. of double bonds	Melting point
Lauric acid	$C_{11}H_{23}COOH$	12	0	44.2
Myristic acid	$C_{13}H_{27}COOH$	14	0	53.9
Palmitic acid	$C_{15}H_{31}COOH$	16	0	63.1
Palmitoleic acid	$C_{15}H_{29}COOH$	16	1	−0.5
Stearic acid	$C_{17}H_{35}COOH$	18	0	69.6
Oleic acid	$C_{17}H_{33}COOH$	18	1	13.4
Linoleic acid	$C_{17}H_{31}COOH$	18	2	−5
Linolenic acid	$C_{17}H_{29}COOH$	18	3	0.11
Arachidic acid	$C_{19}H_{39}COOH$	20	0	76.5
Arachidonic acid	$C_{19}H_{31}COOH$	20	4	−49.5

Table 2.1

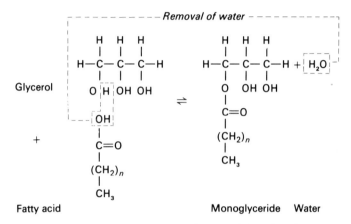

Figure 2.16   Reaction between a fatty acid and glycerol. The other two —OH groups of glycerol can also condense with other fatty acid molecules.

If the fatty acid chain doesn't contain any double bonds, it is said to be a *saturated fatty acid*. If it contains one or more double bonds, it is an *unsaturated fatty acid*.

As glycerol has three —OH groups it usually combines with three fatty acids to form a triglyceride. The fatty acids are joined on to the glycerol in a *condensation* reaction (see Fig. 2.16). The link between the two is called an *ester* bond. The fatty acids can be all of the same type or different to each other.

■ Properties

The specific properties of a lipid depend upon the number and type of fatty acids in it, but since fatty acids are large and non-polar, all simple lipids are totally insoluble in water.

When a lipid is oxidised in a cell, it yields a large amount of energy (more than double the yield of an equal amount of carbohydrate). This is due to the high proportion of hydrogen in the molecule. In addition, lipids can be stored in much larger quantities than carbohydrates. Being insoluble, lipids do not affect the osmotic balance of the cell. Although lipids are harder to mobilise and transport than glucose, they are the main energy storage molecule in many animals.

In mammals, lipids are mainly stored in the fat (adipose tissue), under the skin and around organs such as the heart and kidneys. Lipids have other functions in addition to energy storage. The fat around the kidneys helps to attach them to the dorsal wall of the abdomen and cushions them from impact. The sub-cutaneous fat under the skin is an excellent insulator against heat loss through the body surface.

Q Why do you suppose that plants have no equivalent of adipose tissue? Where in plants do you find stored lipid?

■ Lipids and membranes

Not all lipids contain three fatty acid molecules. Instead, one of the fatty acids may be exchanged for a completely different type of chemical. This can change the properties of the molecule completely. A classic example of this is where phosphate is substituted for a fatty acid to give a *phospholipid*. In this instance, the phosphate group is polar, and this means that it is attracted to water (i.e. it is *hydrophilic*). Remember, though, that it is attached to very large, non-polar lipid molecules which have a distinct aversion to water (i.e they are *hydrophobic*). The result is a rather 'schizophrenic molecule', with one part seeking to interact with water and the other part trying to avoid water (see Fig. 2.17).

So, how can this molecule achieve stability if we put it into water? This problem is solved by a number of molecules gathering together to form a globule with the hydrophilic phosphate 'heads' on the outside and the large hydrophobic fatty acid 'tails' on the inside. This allows the phosphate groups to interact with the water, while the tightly-packed fatty acids inside the globule repel any water molecules. The result is stability and the type of globule (or aggregate) formed is called a *micelle* (see Fig. 2.18).

The tendency of phospholipids to form this type of aggregate in water is of critical importance to life. Each cell needs some form of barrier to keep its biochemicals in one place. This barrier must keep the insides in and the outsides out, yet allow the substances needed by the cell to enter and the wastes and export materials to leave. At the same time the cell must be capable of growth. Such are the requirements of the cell membrane. How are these requirements met?

As always, the functions of a biological structure depend upon its biochemical composition. A simple analysis of membranes shows that they are mainly made up of phospholipid and protein, and so the properties of the membrane must be mainly due to these two molecules.

Look at the structure of the micelle for a moment. If instead of forming a globule the phospholipid molecules are stretched out to form two layers, the interactions with water will still be the same and the resulting *bilayer* will be stable.

In addition, the fatty acid tails of the phospholipid will stop water molecules (and anything dissolved in the water) from getting across this bilayer. The result is a barrier that prevents anything except fat-soluble

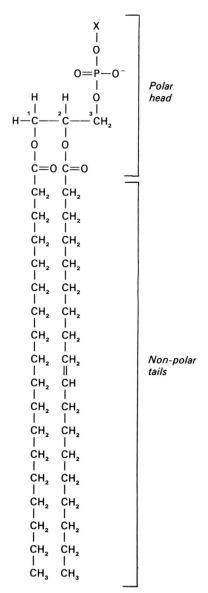

Figure 2.17 General structure of a phospholipid. X can be a variety of chemical groups.

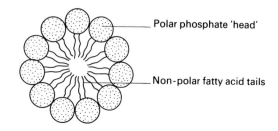

Figure 2.18 A micelle.

22

molecules from crossing, i.e. the requirement for a cell membrane. Evidence indicates that much of the protein in the membrane is involved in allowing substances to cross this barrier in a carefully controlled manner, either by forming *pores* or taking part in *transport mechanisms*.

The membrane can be increased in size by adding more phospholipid, allowing the cell to grow. In addition, phospholipid can be used for membranes inside the cell, so that different biochemical reaction systems can be separated from each other inside 'compartments'. Not all membranes are the same and, by changing the composition, a membrane's properties can be altered. Increasing or reducing the amount of cholesterol, for example, makes the membrane more or less rigid (see Fig. 2.19).

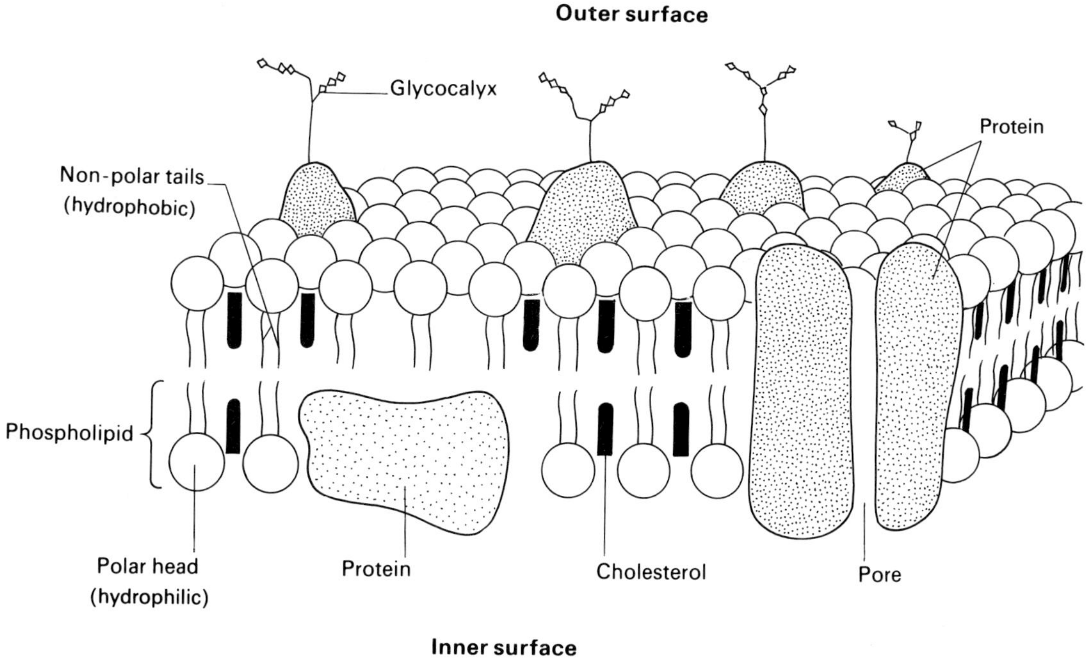

Outer surface

Inner surface

Figure 2.19 The Singer-Nicholson model of membrane structure, proposed in 1972. Called the 'fluid mosaic' model, it has been described as proteins floating in a sea of lipid. It displaced the 'unit membrane' model of Davson and Danielli (1935) who, looking at electron micrographs, thought that the lipid bilayer was sandwiched between two layers of protein. Note the carbohydrate side-chains, i.e. glycocalyx, attached to some of the lipid and protein molecules. These are found on the outside of cell membranes, and act as identification sites so that cells of the same type can recognise each other.

■ Lipids and health

Steroids

Steroids don't have the 'fatty acid and glycerol' structure of other lipids. Instead, they are made up of four interlocking rings with various side groups attached. Some *hormones* (e.g. progesterone and testosterone) and *vitamins* (e.g. vitamin D) fall into this group, as well as *cholesterol* (see Fig. 2.20).

Steroids serve a wide variety of purposes in living systems, but those that have achieved notoriety are the anabolic steroids. These have the effect of increasing muscle size, and so at first sight seem to be of benefit to athletes, weightlifters, etc. They are highly potent chemicals, however, and many are known to have side effects, including kidney damage. It is not therefore on the grounds of 'fair play' alone that the use of these substances is banned in sport.

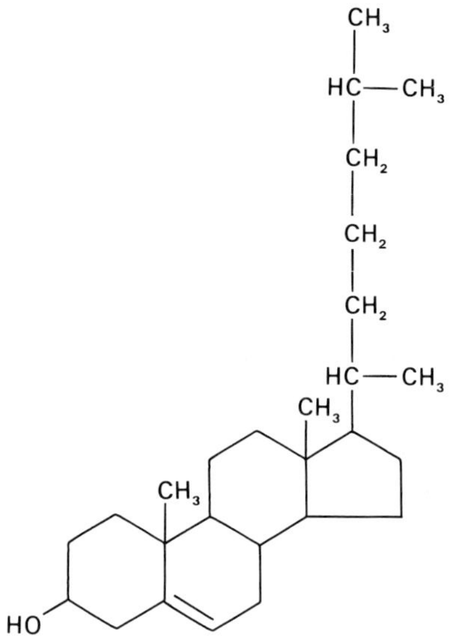

Figure 2.20 Cholesterol.

Lipids and heart disease

One of the major health debates in recent years has concerned the link between fats and heart disease. It has been known for some time that cholesterol can be deposited on the inner walls of blood vessels, reducing their diameter and increasing the likelihood of heart attacks and strokes. People with high blood cholesterol levels are particularly prone to heart disease. It makes sense therefore for people to cut down on cholesterol in the diet. Unfortunately, it is not as simple as that. The body is able to make its own cholesterol, and evidence suggests that the amount made is controlled by the person's genes. Furthermore, a number of studies carried out *seem* to indicate that cutting down cholesterol intake has little effect on the incidence of heart disease in a population. However, some medical scientists think that these results are open to interpretation.

Another area of controversy involves the role of saturated fats in heart disease. Animal products such as butter tend to be high in these fats and research has indicated that diets rich in saturated fats cause a rise in the blood cholesterol level and thus possibly an increased chance of a heart attack. Accordingly,

health authorities have recommended that the level of fat in the diet should be reduced, and of the fat that *is* taken in, more of it should be of the unsaturated variety, particularly polyunsaturates (i.e. fats with two or more double bonds). However, even this last point is open to question. Latest evidence suggests that monounsaturates are the safest ones to eat!

You will have noticed that this section is full of 'possibly's' and 'maybe's'. It is not exactly a satisfactory situation, but that is how things stand at present. The main problem is that there is more than one contributing factor to heart disease. Smoking, high blood pressure, lack of exercise, age, sex and heredity are all believed to be contributing factors. Other factors may include obesity and 'hardness' of drinking water. With so many factors involved you will understand how difficult it is to set up a controlled study. This section has provided you with a very simple summary of a very complicated issue, and ideas are bound to change as more facts become available. The best way to keep up to date in a rapidly changing field such as this one is to read scientific journals like *New Scientist*.

PROTEINS

The name protein comes from the Greek *proteios* meaning 'primary' or of 'of first rank'. In fact, the chemist who coined the word 'protein' in the middle of the last century couldn't have realised how incredibly 'on-target' he was in his choice of name. The bodies of *all* organisms, unicells to eagles, cherry trees to bacteria, humans to viruses, are all full of different proteins. What makes these organisms different? Why do scientists describe our system of life as 'protein-centred'?

You may already have an idea of the answer to the second question. DNA, the genetic substance usually found locked within the chromosomes, turns the genetic blueprint into biochemical reality by *bringing into existence the range of particular proteins that have their own precise biological function* (see Chapter 4). The range of functions is as enormous as it is impressive. All of the *enzymes*, i.e. the biological catalysts that make biochemical reactions happen at realistic speeds, are different proteins (see Chapter 3). The parts of animals, unicells and bacteria that contract and cause movement are made up of *contractile proteins* that interact to cause that contraction. Examples of contractile proteins are *actin* and *myosin* in human muscle fibres. There are also contractile proteins in cilia and flagella. Other proteins, in multicellular animals, carry certain substances around the body. One example of these *transport proteins* is haemoglobin which carries both oxygen and carbon dioxide. If you look back at Fig. 2.19, you will see that 'islands of protein in a sea of phospholipid molecules' is a good description of a cell membrane. These membrane-bound proteins behave as carrier proteins involved in the active transport of molecules and ions in and out of cells.

There are many different functions carried out by *structural proteins*. Where would a bird be without the keratin of its feathers? Hair, horns and hooves are also composed of keratin. Some *hormones* such as insulin are proteins. A further major group of proteins is the set of *immunoproteins*, i.e. the antibodies. These proteins have the essential role of binding to foreign substances, i.e. antigens (for example, the pollen grains in hay fever sufferers), and bringing about their destruction.

You can see from the above paragraphs that there are six categories of proteins:

- enzymes;
- contractile proteins;
- transport proteins;
- structural proteins;
- hormones;
- immunoproteins.

These six categories of proteins cover the range of life processes, i.e. thousands of different proteins each doing specific different jobs. (The idea of 'protein-centred life' is now more than justifiable.) But *how* are proteins different and *how* do these differences give each protein its own unique biological property? To answer these questions we need to look into the chemistry of proteins.

Composition

All proteins contain the elements carbon, hydrogen, oxygen and nitrogen and most of them also contain sulphur. The basic building blocks of proteins, i.e. the monomers, are the *amino acids*. Proteins, like polysaccharides, are polymers. However, polysaccharides are simpler structures as they are usually composed of a single type of monomer (e.g. glucose). Most proteins are built up from a selection of twenty different amino acids.

These twenty commonly occurring amino acids all have the same general formula as shown in Fig. 2.21. They each consist of an acidic carboxyl group, a basic amino group, and a hydrogen atom, all joined on to a carbon atom. The only difference between the various amino acids is the identity of the side chain, or —R group. For example, in the amino acid glycine, —R is another hydrogen atom, in alanine it is a —CH_3 group, and in serine it is a —CH_2OH group.

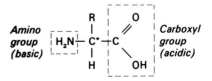

Figure 2.21 General formula of an amino acid. * marks the asymmetric carbon atom. R = a side chain group (see text).

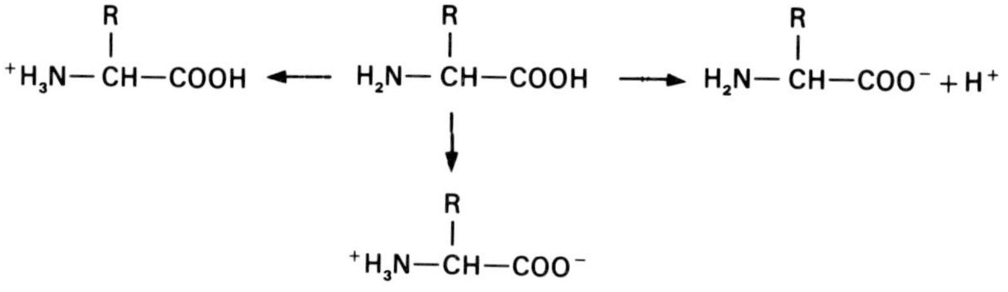

$$^+H_3N-CH-COOH \longleftarrow H_2N-CH-COOH \longrightarrow H_2N-CH-COO^- + H^+$$

$$^+H_3N-CH-COO^-$$

(with R groups above each CH)

Figure 2.22 The various states of ionisation of an amino acid. When both amino and carboxyl groups carry a charge this is called a **zwitterion**. Depending on the type of amino acid, the R group can also carry a charge.

Except in the case of glycine, the carbon atom to which the various groups are joined is an asymmetric carbon. This means that D- and L-isomers can exist, as is the case with the monosaccharides. However, in most living organisms (except for certain microbes) only the L-isomer of an amino acid is found. This is the exact opposite case to that seen in the carbohydrates.

As you can see from Fig. 2.22, each amino acid has the ability to give out a hydrogen ion from the carboxyl group, and take in a hydrogen ion onto the amino group. A molecule with both acidic and basic properties is called *amphoteric*. Whether the amino group gains a proton or the carboxyl group loses a proton (or both occur at the same time) depends on the pH of the surrounding solution.

Amino acids are joined together by a condensation reaction between the amino group of one acid and the carboxyl group of another. The bond formed between two amino acids is known as a peptide bond (see Fig. 2.23).

The resulting molecule is a *dipeptide*. If a lot more amino acids are linked together a *polypeptide* is formed. Still more and eventually you have a protein.

When does a polypeptide become a protein? It is difficult to say. One of the smallest proteins is *insulin*, with 51 amino acids, but there are polypeptides much bigger than this. As a crude rule, you could take the difference as being that a protein is *functional*, while polypeptides are more often *components* of proteins. (Insulin, for example, has two polypeptide chains.) The number of amino acids in different proteins varies widely, but ranges from about 40 up to several thousand in the larger, more complex proteins. The number of different amino acids found in any individual type of protein also varies, and animal proteins usually show a wider variety of amino acids than plant proteins. This gives rise to the unscientific terms *first* and *second-class proteins* which you may have seen in some books on nutrition. It doesn't mean anything except that if you are a vegetarian it is a good idea to eat a range of plant foods to make sure that you get enough of *each* amino acid (see Chapter 5).

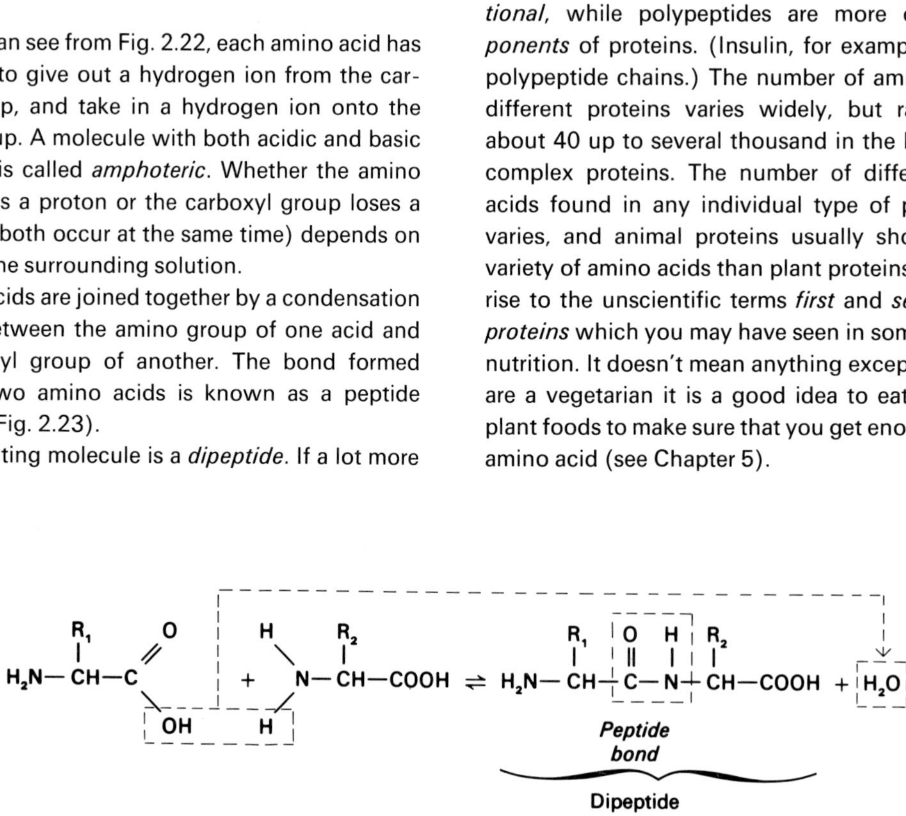

$$H_2N-CH-C \overset{O}{\underset{OH}{\big\|}} + N-CH-COOH \rightleftharpoons H_2N-CH-C-N-CH-COOH + H_2O$$

Peptide bond

Dipeptide

Figure 2.23 Formation of the peptide bond.

26

■ Protein analysis

How can you determine which amino acids are present in a particular protein? Two techniques can be used:

- chromatography;
- electrophoresis.

Chromatography involves separating out the amino acids on filter paper using a solvent. The distance moved by the amino acids will be determined by its affinity to 'stick' to the paper or dissolve in the solvent. The position of the amino acids can be found using a special dye.

The first step is to hydrolyse all the peptide bonds in the protein so that the individual amino acids are released. This can be done by heating the protein. The mixture of amino acids is placed drop by drop onto a sheet of filter paper, allowing the solvent to evaporate in between adding each drop. The result is a highly concentrated area of amino acids. The strip of filter paper is then placed in a tank containing a suitable solvent. As the solvent moves along the filter paper (either up or down, depending on the type of tank being used), interactions will occur between the amino acids and the two phases that they are exposed to, i.e. the moving solvent phase and the stationary paper phase. Those amino acids which dissolve readily in the solvent will move along the paper with it, while those amino acids that 'stick' (i.e. *absorb*) to the paper will tend to stay where they are. Most amino acids fall between these two extremes. The distance moved by the amino acid along the paper will be determined by its relative affinities for each of the two phases. By the time the solvent has neared the end of the paper, the amino acids in the mixture will have been separated out from each other. The locations of the amino acids can be made visible by adding a reagent such as nin-

hydrin which will give a coloured spot on the paper. (*Caution*: ninhydrin is a poisonous substance.)

For any given solvent, the relative distance moved by a particular amino acid will always be the same, and can thus be used to identify it. This relative distance is given a value, known as the R_f value, and can be calculated using the formula:

$$R_f = \frac{\text{distance moved by spot}}{\text{distance moved by solvent}}$$

By redissolving each spot in solvent and measuring the colour intensity with a colorimeter, the amount of each amino acid present can also be calculated.

Using paper as the stationary phase is the simplest type of chromatography. Much more efficient techniques have been developed, such as gas-liquid chromatography which is able to detect and separate minute amounts of substances in a mixture.

Electrophoresis involves separating out the amino acids on filter paper by exposing them to an electrical field. The distance and direction moved by the amino acid will be determined by its charge. The position of the amino acids is found using a special dye.

As we have seen in the case of amino acids, certain molecules often carry charges on their amino or carboxyl groups, depending on the pH of the solution in which they are found. In addition, the —R groups of many amino acids, such as lysine, can also carry a charge. By exposing a mixture of amino acids to an electrical field, those with a negative charge will move towards the positively charged anode while those with a positive charge will move towards the cathode. The more highly charged the amino acid, the farther it will migrate in a given time. The distance moved at a particular pH is characteristic and will identify the amino acid once it is developed with ninhydrin.

Although it can be used for identifying amino acids, electrophoresis is more useful for separating and identifying the constituents of mixtures of proteins. Electrophoresis is often used in hospital laboratories to analyse blood plasma, where the presence of an unusual protein can indicate or confirm that a patient is suffering from a particular condition. For example, a high level of the enzyme *acid phosphatase* in the blood is characteristic of prostate gland trouble in males.

■ Structure

As with the other types of molecules we have looked at so far, the structure of proteins determines their properties, which in turn determines their uses in living systems. The shape of a protein molecule is very complicated and in order to understand this shape fully, we will look at it under the following levels of complexity:

- primary structure;
- secondary structure;
- tertiary structure;
- quaternary structure.

Primary structure

The primary structure describes the number, the type and the sequence of amino acids found in the polypeptide chain. Frederick Sanger in 1954 was the first to describe the primary structure of insulin.

As you will see later, the primary structure of the protein determines its eventual conformation. Changing the sequence of amino acids in the chain even slightly can change the shape and so alter the whole way in which the protein behaves.

Secondary structure

Most proteins contain at least some areas where the polypeptide chain is folded in a regular manner. These areas are stabilised by interactions between some of the amino acids found there and represent the secondary structure of proteins. There are two forms of secondary structure known as the *α-helix* and the *β-pleated sheet*. Both of these structures were described by Pauling and Corey in 1951.

The existence of the α-helix was first suggested from the building of molecular models of polypeptide chains. At about the same time, the technique of **X-ray diffraction** indicated the presence of helical regions in real protein molecules.

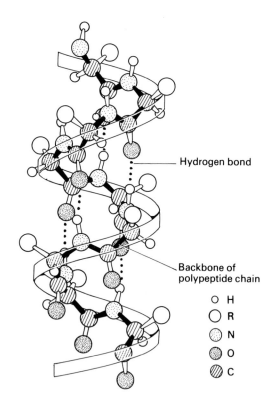

Figure 2.25 The α-helix.

- Hydrogen bond
- Backbone of polypeptide chain

○ H
○ R
◎ N
◉ O
◎ C

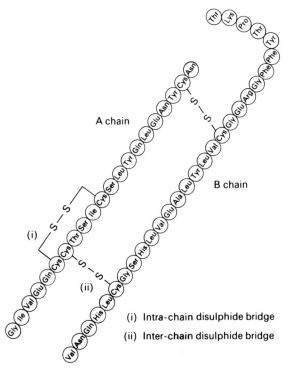

(i) Intra-chain disulphide bridge
(ii) Inter-chain disulphide bridge

A chain

B chain

Figure 2.24 The primary structure of insulin showing the two polypeptide chains. Each unit represents an amino acid. You can identify Gly (glycine), Ala (alanine) and Ser (serine).

X-ray diffraction involves making a crystal of the molecule to be studied. X-rays are then beamed at the crystal from various angles. Some of the rays are scattered by the atoms in the molecule and these rays are 'registered' on a photographic plate (i.e. X-rays fog the film). By identifying where the X-ray has struck the plate, the angle through which the beam was deflected can be calculated. Eventually, the three-dimensional shape of the whole molecule can be determined.

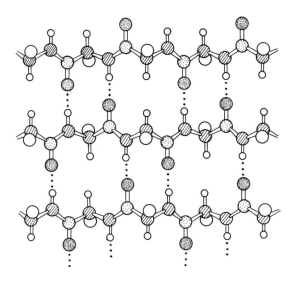

Figure 2.26 The β-pleated sheet. The key in this figure is the same as the one shown in Fig. 2.25.

The α-helix is a right-handed spiral of amino acids, with the —R groups projecting from it in various directions. The whole structure is held in shape by hydrogen bonds between the —C═O group of one amino acid and the —NH group of another one further along the chain (see Fig. 2.25).

The β-pleated sheet is formed by areas of the polypeptide chain lining up alongside each other. The chains, which have a zigzag shape, are held in place by hydrogen bonds. The resulting structure is strong and flexible. Silk is an excellent example of a protein containing high levels of the β-pleated sheet.

Proteins whose overall shape is made up almost entirely of a secondary structure are called *fibrous* proteins. **Keratin** is a fibrous protein that is almost pure α-helix.

Keratin is the protein found in hair, bone, horn and feathers. The overall 'hardness' of the structure depends on the amount of disulphide bridging holding the different molecules together (see later). The more disulphide bridges there are, the stronger the structure. Hairdressers can put waves into hair by subjecting the hair to fairly drastic conditions which break the disulphide bridges. The bridges reform once the hair (and therefore the keratin molecules) has been placed into the new style. The hair will remain in this style until it grows out.

Another fibrous protein that should be mentioned here is collagen. Each molecule is made up of three helically coiled polypeptide chains (not an α-helix) wound around each other and hydrogen bonded together to form a superhelix. The result is a strong, inelastic structure, such as is found in tendons.

Tertiary structure

The tertiary structure is the three-dimensional shape of the whole protein in space. It's held in this shape by various types of bonding. These are:

- hydrogen bonds;
- disulphide bridges;
- ionic interactions;
- hydrophilic/hydrophobic interactions.

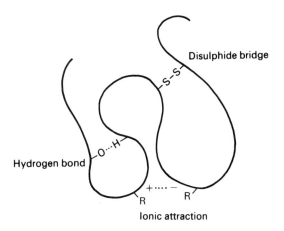

Figure 2.27 The forces that give the shape (conformation) of the protein molecule.

Hydrogen bonds (see Fig. 2.27).

Disulphide bridges (see Fig. 2.27). One of the amino acids, cysteine, has sulphur in its side chain. If two cysteine residues in the polypeptide chain are brought closely together, a reaction can occur between two sulphur atoms to form a strong covalent bond between the two amino acids. The disulphide bridge can either form a loop in the polypeptide chain or help to hold two chains together, as seen in insulin (see Fig. 2.24).

Ionic interactions. If two oppositely charged —R groups are close together, an attraction will take place. Conversely, there will be repulsion between two similarly charged —R groups.

Hydrophilic/hydrophobic interactions. Some amino acids have non-polar —R groups (i.e. hydrophobic) and others have polar —R groups (i.e. hydrophilic). As a result, the protein tends to fold in such a way that the hydrophobic groups are clustered at the centre of the molecule and so they don't come into contact with water, while the hydrophilic groups are arranged on the outside of the molecule.

These and other forces in the molecule have the net effect of holding the protein in a specific, closely defined shape. Proteins which show this complex folding are referred to as *globular proteins*. The first protein for which the tertiary structure was described was *myoglobin*, the protein that stores oxygen in muscle (J.C. Kendrew in 1959, using X-ray diffraction).

Quaternary structure
Many globular proteins are composed of more than one polypeptide chain. The way in which these subunits fit together is termed the quaternary structure. The first protein to have its quaternary structure described was *haemoglobin* (Max Perutz, in 1960).

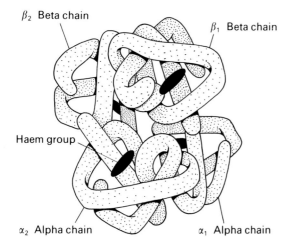

β_2 Beta chain
β_1 Beta chain
Haem group
α_2 Alpha chain
α_1 Alpha chain

Figure 2.28 Haemoglobin. This is a large protein made up of four polypeptide chains — two alpha and two beta. A molecule of oxygen can combine to each haem group.

You should now be able to see how the primary structure of the protein determines its overall shape, and thus its function. It is the presence of particular amino acids at particular points on the chain that enable the bonds to be formed and give a particular conformation. Changing the primary structure even slightly can have dramatic effects on the protein, especially if one of the amino acids changed is involved in forming one of the structure-maintaining bonds. A good example of this is seen in the case of haemoglobin. Replacing a single glutamic acid residue with a valine in each beta chain results in the condition called *sickle-cell anaemia*. In this condition, altered haemoglobin is far less efficient at taking up oxygen and the red cells become deformed. This can cause blockages in minor blood vessels which are usually fatal.

■ Properties of proteins

Solubility
Despite their large size, globular proteins are reasonably soluble in water due to the number of polar groups present at their surface. They are too big to dissolve properly to give a true solution, however, but instead form *colloids*. A colloid is a mixture of two substances which are immiscible (in this case, protein and water), but where the particles of one are too large to settle out and so remain suspended indefinitely. Colloid particles tend to be between 1×10^{-4} and 1×10^{-6} mm in diameter. Cytoplasm is a classic example of a colloid in which water is the *dispersion medium* and proteins are the *dispersed phase*.

Fibrous proteins are insoluble in water as they tend to have a large number of exposed hydrophobic amino acids in their structure.

Denaturation
As you will have seen, the shape of globular proteins is maintained in particular by various types of bond. Any factor that causes disruption of these bonds is therefore bound to result in a certain amount of unfolding in the protein chain, i.e. it denatures. Heat and extremes of pH are the two main conditions which cause denaturing of proteins (see Chapter 4).

CHAPTER 3

ENZYMES - CATALYSTS AND CONTROLLERS

■ INTRODUCTION

Picture an organism as being composed of thousands of chemical reactions held together in the same place. If we take just one of those reactions, e.g. the breakdown of poisonous hydrogen peroxide into water and oxygen, a major problem becomes apparent straight away. Left to itself, the stable peroxide shows little tendency to breakdown. After a few weeks something may begin to happen to it, but by that time the cell would have formed enough of the chemical to prove fatal. Obviously, something is required to speed things up.

Q In chemistry labs, heat is often used to make reactions occur faster. Could living organisms use the same technique?

To an extent they can and do, for example when snakes move into sunlight. However, above a certain level the energy given by the heat is enough to break the weak bonds that hold molecules such as proteins in their specific shape, and denaturation occurs. This denaturation is lethal to the organism (see page 30).

In industrial processes, certain chemicals known as catalysts can be added to speed up the rate of a reaction. Adding iron filings to hydrogen peroxide, for example, will immediately cause bubbles of oxygen to be given off. Living systems have their own highly efficient catalysts – the enzymes which provide the major means of controlling the metabolic reactions of the cell.

■ STRUCTURE AND OCCURRENCE

All enzymes are globular or conjugated proteins, with molecular masses between about 10 000 and 500 000. Although the chain of amino acids making up the enzyme's structure is folded in an apparently random manner, the three-dimensional shape, held by forces such as hydrogen bonds, is critical for its efficient functioning.

Enzymes occur both inside cells (intracellular) and outside cells (extracellular), i.e. secreted by cells. Inside cells, enzymes are often found fixed into the membrane and this keeps them in one place (e.g. where one enzyme needs to work closely with other enzymes). Although each cell in an organism potentially has the ability to manufacture all of the enzymes found in that organism, the cell will only make those enzymes which are concerned with its own survival or function. This feature has proved to be a useful diagnostic aid in hospitals, where blood can be screened for the presence of unusual enzymes. For example, the graph shows the distribution of three enzymes that are usually found in the blood after a certain type of heart attack called a myocardial infarction, when the heart muscle is damaged. By measuring the level of each enzyme, the type, severity and time of attack can be determined.

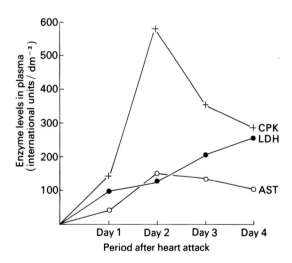

Key CPK = Creatine phosphokinase LDH = Lactate dehydrogenase AST = Aspartate aminotransferase

Figure 3.1 Graph showing plasma levels of CPK, LDH and AST after myocardial infarction. These enzymes are released by the damaged heart muscle.

■ HOW ENZYMES WORK

For this general reaction the energy changes that occur are shown in Fig. 3.2. The solid line curve shows the uncatalysed reaction. The chemical bonds holding the atoms of the molecules together are difficult to break, and an input of energy, the *activation energy*, is needed to get the reaction going. This is true whether it involves the conversion of complex molecules into simpler ones or vice-versa.

Q Look at the graph opposite. Is this an exergonic (energy-releasing) or endergonic (energy-requiring) reaction?

Look at the graph again. Is this reaction likely to be easily reversible?

Enzymes decrease the activation energy needed for a reaction to take place (see dotted line curve in Fig. 3.2). It seems likely that enzymes are able to lower the activation energy in two ways. Firstly, by binding to the reacting molecules, i.e. the *substrates*, so bringing them into close contact with each other and thus making a reaction more likely, and secondly, by somehow creating an environment around the substrates which stresses and destabilises the bonds. The sequence of events is usually summarised as follows:

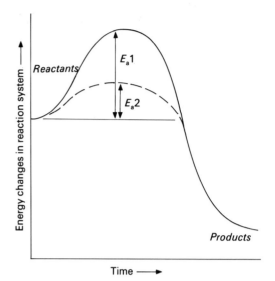

E_a1 = Activation energy for uncatalysed reaction
E_a2 = Activation energy for the same reaction, but enzyme-catalysed

Figure 3.2 The effects of an enzyme upon activation energy. There is a substantial loss of energy as reactants become products. Thus the reaction is exergonic and not readily reversible.

$$\text{Enzyme} + \text{Substrate} \rightleftharpoons \text{Enzyme-substrate} \rightleftharpoons \text{Enzyme-product} \rightleftharpoons \text{Enzyme} + \text{Product}$$
$$\text{complex} \qquad\qquad \text{complex}$$

Figure 3.3 How an enzyme works.

Q Try to decide what may happen if the concentration of product is allowed to build up.

As can be seen, all the stages in the sequence are in theory (and often in practice) reversible. Enzymes don't affect the balance point, i.e. the *point of equilibrium*, in a reversible reaction, and so if the products aren't removed in some way the enzyme will begin to convert them back.

The substrate binds to a certain region of the enzyme molecule called the *active site*. This site is made up of a number of amino acids in the enzyme's chain. These amino acids form a 'pocket' or active site (see Fig. 3.4).

Enzymes are often highly *specific* in the types of reaction that they catalyse. Lactic dehydrogenase in respiration, for example, will convert L-lactic acid into pyruvic acid, but have no effect on the D-isomer of lactic acid. To explain this Fischer, as far back as 1894, proposed the *lock and key* theory (see Fig. 3.5).

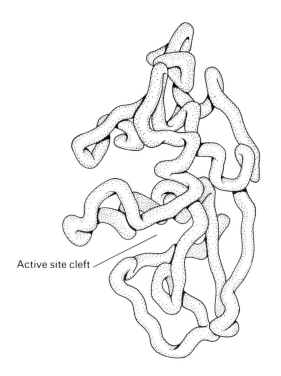

Active site cleft

This theory suggests that the active site of the enzyme (i.e. the lock) has a particular shape and will only accept an appropriately shaped substrate (i.e. the key) before anything happens; hence the specificity of the enzyme. Modern techniques such as X-ray diffraction analysis have shown this theory to be basically correct. But it now seems probable that in the case of most enzymes, the match between the substrate and the active site is not quite so exact. Instead, the shape of the active site is altered to fit the substrate molecule as it attaches. Studies of some enzymes have shown that the change in shape is small, but serves to bind the substrate molecules tightly. In addition, moulding of the active site around the substrate could well put a strain on the substrate's bonds, weakening them and making a reaction more likely. This is known as the *induced fit* theory (see Fig. 3.6).

Figure 3.4 Lysozyme, showing the position of the active site. This enzyme helps kill bacteria by breaking down their cell walls and is often found in tears.

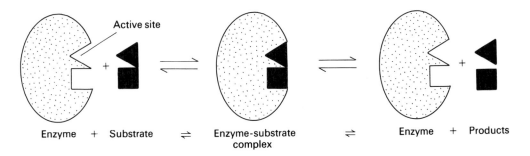

| Enzyme | + | Substrate | ⇌ | Enzyme-substrate complex | ⇌ | Enzyme | + | Products |

Figure 3.5 The lock and key theory.

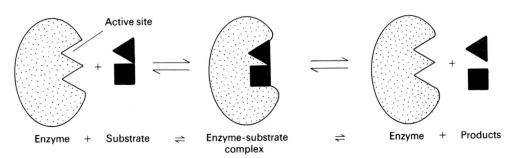

| Enzyme | + | Substrate | ⇌ | Enzyme-substrate complex | ⇌ | Enzyme | + | Products |

Figure 3.6 The induced fit theory.

On the face of it, it may seem more efficient to allow an enzyme to catalyse several different types of reactions, and so save on the number of enzymes that need to be made.

Q Why is this not so? How would the enzyme 'know' which particular reaction needed catalysing within the cell?

Overall control of reactions would be impossible if enzymes were not so specific. The rule of 'one reaction, one enzyme' applies to most reactions.

Certain enzymes will only work when another, non-protein molecule known as a cofactor is present. There are two kinds of cofactors. One type is firmly attached to the enzyme molecule and is known as a *prosthetic group*. Examples of prosthetic groups include metal ions such as Zn^{2+}, Cu^{2+} and K^+, and haem groups. They may serve one of two possible roles, either helping to bind the enzyme and substrate together, or acting as the catalytic group itself. The iron atoms of catalase, the enzyme which catalyses the breakdown of our toxic hydrogen peroxide, are an example of the latter.

Coenzymes, however, are molecules which are not permanently attached to the enzyme. They usually act as intermediate carriers, transferring electrons or chemical groups from one enzyme to another in a sequence of reactions. The most well known of these is nicotinamide adenine dinucleotide (NAD^+). NAD^+ is vital for transferring hydrogen around from one stage to another in respiration and will be discussed in more detail in later chapters. Many vitamins either act as coenzymes or are needed to make them, e.g. vitamin B_3 (nicotinic acid) is a vital part of the NAD^+ molecule.

Enzymes are highly efficient, often increasing the rate of a reaction by a factor anywhere between 10^7 and 10^{12}. What's more, they aren't used up in the reaction, and after converting one substrate molecule into the product will then go on to act on another one. Catalase, for example, can break down six million molecules of hydrogen peroxide per minute in optimum conditions.

Q If an enzyme converts molecule A into molecule B, how could you measure its rate of reaction? (Suggest ways to either measure the rate at which the product appears, or the rate at which the substrate disappears.)

■ FACTORS AFFECTING ENZYME ACTIVITY

There are several factors which can influence the rate at which enzyme-catalysed reactions proceed. Most of these are of considerable importance in living organisms, and must be carefully controlled. The main ones are as follows:

■ Concentration of substrate

If more substrate is added to a reaction system, the following pattern is seen.

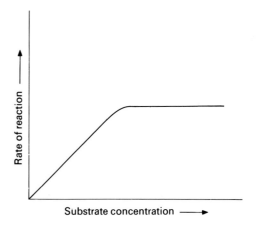

Figure 3.7 Graph of substrate concentration versus rate of reaction.

As you can see, the rate of reaction increases as more enzyme-substrate complex is formed. After a certain point the rate of reaction levels off and won't go any higher no matter how much more the substrate concentration is increased. This is because there is a limit to the number of substrate molecules an enzyme can change into product in a given time. Once this maximum is reached, the enzyme can't work any faster, regardless of now many substrate molecules are present. The enzyme is said to be *saturated*.

This rise in reaction rate caused by increasing the substrate availability is one of the reasons why glucose is not stored in high levels in most cells, as it takes part in so many reactions. If glucose was available in high concentrations, many of these reactions would happen rapidly whether they were needed or not and the cell would lose control.

Q How has this problem been solved in cells such as liver and skeletal muscle which need to have high levels of glucose available?

The glucose in these cells is made unavailable by converting it into insoluble glycogen which only certain enzymes such as glycogen phosphorylase can break down. By controlling this enzyme, the cell controls the level of free glucose available. The plant equivalent of glycogen is starch.

■ **Concentration of enzyme**

In any chemical reaction, altering the concentration of reactants changes the rate at which the reaction takes place. Those reactions catalysed by enzymes are no exception. If the amount of enzyme present is increased, the reaction speeds up proportionally. This is true as long as there is plenty of substrate to act upon (see Fig. 3.8.).

It is just like using a bus (i.e. the enzyme) to take a thousand fans (i.e. the substrate molecules) to a football match (i.e. arrival = product). One bus will only do the job slowly, the two buses will do it twice as quickly, three will achieve three times the rate, and so on. However, if there are only twenty fans to start with increasing the number of buses won't have any great effect.

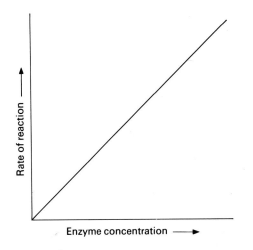

Figure 3.8 Graph of enzyme concentration versus rate of reaction.

■ **Temperature**

With most chemical reactions, raising the temperature will increase the rate of reaction. This is true of enzyme catalysed reactions, but only up to a point. Examine the graph in Fig. 3.9.

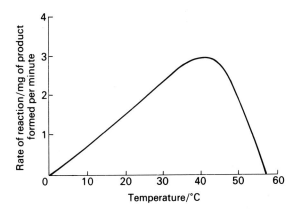

Figure 3.9 Graph of temperature versus rate of reaction.

As you can see, initially as the temperature is increased so the rate of reaction goes up. You would expect this as the number of molecules possessing the amount of activation energy needed to react is being increased as more heat energy is supplied. The temperature coefficient, or Q_{10}, is used to show the relationship between the reaction rate and a 10°C rise in temperature.

$$Q_{10} = \frac{\text{Rate of reaction at t°C} + 10°C}{\text{Rate of reaction at t°C}}$$

Q Calculate the value of Q_{10} for the reaction in Fig. 3.9 if the temperature is raised from 25°C to 35°C. (See answer page 36.)

Q For most enzyme reactions, Q_{10} is about 2, i.e. for every 10°C rise in temperature, the reaction rate doubles. If the reaction above was kept at 35°C for a long period of time, and then Q_{10} was calculated, it would appear to be a lot lower than 2. Why? (Hint: think of other factors).

As the reaction proceeds, the level of substrate would fall as it is converted into product by the enzyme. As the rate of reaction is also dependent on the concentration of substrate, this too would fall – nothing to do with the effect of temperature. Hence the need for controls, i.e. keep all experimental factors constant except for the one being investigated.

After a certain point, the rate of reaction begins to fall drastically. At about 60°C, when you might think things should really be moving, there is no reaction at all. Why not? The answer lies in the fact that all enzymes are proteins. As with other proteins an enzyme has a very specific shape, and is held in this shape by strong disulphide bridges and much weaker hydrogen bonds, ionic interactions, etc. Heating the enzymes above a certain level will provide enough energy to break these weaker bonds and unfold the amino acid chain. When this happens the enzyme is said to be *denatured*. The enzyme is effectively destroyed, and usually will not work again even if the temperature falls.

The graph in Fig. 3.9 shows that there is an *optimum* temperature for enzyme activity, i.e. warm enough to make the reaction proceed rapidly, but not hot enough to denature the enzyme. For most of our enzymes, this optimum lies in the range of 37°–43°C. It is no coincidence that the body temperature of humans is about 37°C. In fact, endothermic animals (those organisms such as birds and mammals that can maintain a body temperature independent of that of their surroundings) have a number of specialised features to keep their temperature at the optimum point. Even ectotherms (those animals such as lizards whose body temperature fluctuates with that of their environment) make use of sun and shade to maintain their temperature within this range.

Briefly consider some of the features which endotherms have to maintain a constant body temperature. The list is considerable, feathers and fur for insulation is just the beginning. There is also shivering, sweating, changing the metabolic rate, varying the blood flow to the skin, and so on. All of these features show how important it is to the animal to keep its body temperature at the optimum level. This thermoregulation is vital. If the body temperature of an ectotherm falls, the rate of metabolism decreases and the animal becomes more and more sluggish.

If the body temperature of an organism rises even slightly above the optimum, the effects can be catastrophic. All enzyme-catalysed reaction rates will increase, and as one of the main by-products of metabolism is heat, the body temperature will rise further. This causes another increase in the metabolic rate, producing more heat, and so on. Very rapidly the temperature is reached where the enzymes denature and the organism dies. In humans, this runaway upward spiral begins at about 44°C. (This point was raised in Chapter 1 pages 9 and 10.)

Interestingly, bacteria have been found living in hot water springs, where the temperature is about 65°C. Tests have shown that their enzymes are more resistant to heat denaturation than the corresponding enzymes found in other bacteria.

■ The pH of the surroundings

Most enzymes are severely affected by the concentration of H^+ ions in the solution around them. Many of the bonds holding the enzyme in its three-dimensional shape depend upon the presence of ionic charges on amino acids at particular points. Changing the pH even slightly can alter these charges, causing the ionic bonds to disappear and the enzyme to denature. In addition, enzymes usually need charges at the active site. Change these charges or take them away and the enzyme won't be able to affect the substrate.

All enzymes have an optimum pH at which they will work most effectively. For most enzymes, this value lies between 7.2 and 7.4, i.e. cell pH. There are exceptions to this, however as Fig. 3.10 shows.

 Does the graph in Fig. 3.10 explain why HCl is secreted in the stomach but not in the saliva?

Answer (from page 35)

Number of mg of product formed per minute
at 25°C = 1.8

Number of mg of product formed per minute
at 35°C = 2.9

$$Q_{10} = 2.9/1.8$$

$$= 1.6$$

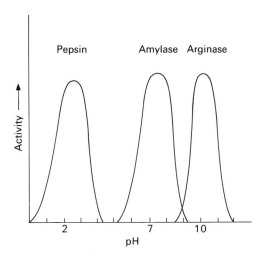

Figure 3.10 pH profiles for pepsin, amylase and arginase. Pepsin is a protein hydrolysing enzyme and amylase hydrolyses starch. Arginase is involved in making urea in the kidneys.

It is clear, then, that organisms need to keep their internal pH constant otherwise their enzymes denature. This can be done in two ways:

● Excretion of acidic or alkaline chemicals from the body;
● Use of buffers. These are chemicals which resist changes in pH. Many blood proteins, including haemoglobin, perform this function (see the Guide to Chemistry, page 120).

Keeping the temperature and pH within very narrow limits is a vital part of *homeostasis* (i.e. maintaining a constant internal environment).

■ Inhibitors

An inhibitor is a substance which interferes with an enzyme's activity, either slowing the rate of reaction down, or in some cases stopping it altogether. Many substances found in cells can act as inhibitors, and as you will see later in this chapter these substances play an important role in regulating biochemical pathways. Other chemicals that can act as inhibitors, however, are rarely found in living systems, and it is this group that is discussed below. Interestingly, many of these chemicals have turned out to be useful laboratory 'tools' when investigating phenomena such as respiration and enzyme activity. These inhibitors fall into two groups, reversible and irreversible.

Reversible inhibitors
These are substances which reduce an enzyme's activity by affecting its ability to bind to its substrate. When the inhibitor is removed, the enzyme's activity is restored. There are two types of reversible inhibitors, *competitive* and *non-competitive*.

Competitive reversible inhibition
The enzyme succinic dehydrogenase catalyses the conversion of succinic acid into fumaric acid by removing hydrogen from it (see Fig. 3.11).

If malonic acid is added to this system, the rate of reaction immediately slows down. Why? Look at the structure of malonic acid (Fig. 3.12).

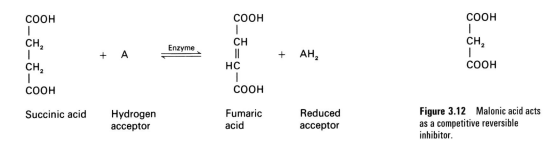

Succinic acid   Hydrogen acceptor   Fumaric acid   Reduced acceptor

Figure 3.11 Action of succinic dehydrogenase. You will meet this enzyme again in Chapter 6.

Figure 3.12 Malonic acid acts as a competitive reversible inhibitor.

As you can see, malonic acid is very similar to succinic acid. So similar in fact that it is able to temporarily bind on to the active site of the dehydrogenase enzyme. Nothing happens to the bound malonic acid and it is soon released, but while it is bound the active site is blocked and so the correct substrate (i.e. succinic acid) can't bind and the overall reaction slows down. The enzyme isn't damaged, it is just blocked up. It is like putting the wrong key in a lock; the door won't open, but while the wrong key is there the right key can't be used. Because the inhibitor is competing with the substrate for the active site, it is known as a competitive inhibitor. The more inhibitor molecules that are present, the greater the competition and the slower the reaction proceeds.

You have read that competitive inhibition can be relieved by removing the inhibitor. How else could you do it? Add more substrate. This would increase the odds of the enzyme meeting a substrate molecule rather than an inhibitor and the reaction rate would speed up again.

Non-competitive reversible inhibitors

A non-competitive reversible inhibitor binds to an enzyme regardless of how much substrate is available, and once attached often has a tendency to stay there. It may or may not attach itself at the active site, depending on the type of inhibitor it is, but in either case the enzyme is inactivated. If enough inhibitor is used, the reaction stops completely.

Examples of these inhibitors include arsenic, silver, mercury and lead ions. These inhibitors combine with the disulphide bridges of enzymes. As disulphide bridges generally serve to lock the protein into a particular shape, their alteration will result in an enzyme molecule with a lot more 'wobble' in it (see Fig 3.13). The substrate is less able to bind to the active site which is continually changing shape, and the enzyme activity is reduced. Another example is cyanide, which forms a complex with the Fe^{3+} ion. This ion is very important to the activity of enzymes such as catalase.

All of the substances mentioned here are highly poisonous. Although they are classed as being reversible, in practice it would take drastically changed conditions to remove them from an enzyme. In living systems, they can be considered irreversible!

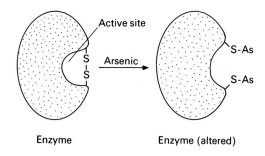

Figure 3.13 The effect of arsenic on enzyme structure. The 'locking' effect of the disulphide bridge has been removed, causing the active site to vary from its specific shape and so altering the enzyme.

Irreversible inhibitors

These bond covalently to the enzyme structure, permanently inactivating it. Again, these molecules are highly poisonous. Examples include nerve gases which bind to enzymes present in the nerve synapses, producing effects which are lethal to the organism.

However, enzyme inhibitors do have their uses. One of the earliest drugs used to treat bacterial infections was sulphanilamide. Bacteria need a substance called p-aminobenzoic acid to make a vital coenzyme, folic acid. The enzyme which normally converts the aminobenzoic acid to folic acid binds the sulphanilamide at its active site as it has a similar structure (see Fig. 3.14). The result is that the bacterium is unable to make enough folic acid. Humans don't have this enzyme and so are unaffected by the drug.

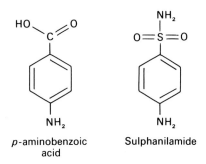

p-aminobenzoic acid   Sulphanilamide

Figure 3.14 Sulphanilamide acts as an irreversible inhibitor due to its similar structure to p-aminobenzoic acid.

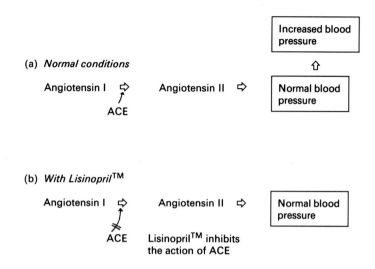

(a) *Normal conditions*

Angiotensin I ⇨ Angiotensin II ⇨ | Normal blood pressure |

ACE

Increased blood pressure

⇧

(b) *With Lisinopril™*

Angiotensin I ⇨ Angiotensin II ⇨ | Normal blood pressure |

ACE

Lisinopril™ inhibits the action of ACE

Figure 3.15 Action of Lisinopril™

More recently, the drug Lisinopril™ has been very effective in lowering high blood pressure. The body produces a substance called angiotensin II which causes blood vessels to constrict and so raises the blood pressure. This substance is made from a chemical called angiotensin I by an angiotensin converting enzyme (ACE). Lisinopril specifically inhibits ACE causing the level of angiotensin II to fall and the blood pressure to drop (see Fig. 3.15).

■ Activators

If certain enzymes were made in their active form they would cause severe damage to the cell. Proteases such as pepsin, for example, don't distinguish between vital cell proteins and proteins to be digested, they just attack all peptide bonds. To stop this from happening, these enzymes are made and stored in an inactive form as *enzyme precursors*, and are only 'switched on' by an activator when and where they are required. With the enzyme pepsin, hydrochloric acid in the stomach is the initial activator, although in the case of other enzymes it is often another enzyme that carries out this role (e.g. an enzyme converts prothrombin to thrombin in blood clotting, and enterokinase in the small intestine converts trypsinogen to trypsin).

■ ENZYMES AS CONTROLLERS OF METABOLISM

At any moment in time there are hundreds of chemical reactions going on in a cell, some manufacturing new molecules, others breaking them down. Most of these reactions are parts of larger pathways, and the pathways themselves may have side branches, other pathways feeding in to them, and so on. This gives a lot more flexibility to the cell by allowing it to switch chemicals from one pathway to another as requirements change, but it does make things very complicated. In fact, a chart of a cell's metabolic routes makes a map of Euston Station's railway lines look positively simple. How, then, is the cell able to exert overall control of this potential chaos and determine not only which reactions proceed at any one time, but how fast they actually happen?

The answer must be to control the enzymes. Remember, each reaction in an organism is catalysed by an enzyme – if you haven't got an enzyme for a reaction you can't carry out the reaction. Furthermore, each enzyme will only catalyse one type of reaction, i.e. they are highly specific. Control the enzyme and you control that particular reaction.

Take a look at a hypothetical branching pathway system as shown in Fig. 3.16.

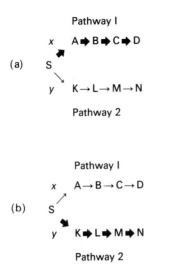

Pathway I

x A ➡ B ➡ C ➡ D

(a) S

y K → L → M → N

Pathway 2

Pathway I

x A → B → C → D

(b) S

y K ➡ L ➡ M ➡ N

Pathway 2

Figure 3.16 Two possible fates of substrate (S). x and y are enzymes that catalyse reactions in Pathways 1 and 2 respectively.

In Fig 3.16(a) the enzyme activity in reaction x is high, while that in reaction y is less so. The result, therefore, is that most of substrate S goes into pathway 1 and chemical D is the main product. If cell demand for product N should suddenly increase, reducing the rate of reaction of x and increasing that of y will result in more of N being made as shown in Fig. 3.16(b)

How can the enzymes be controlled? There are two main ways:

- controlling the amount of enzyme present;
- switching the enzyme on and off.

■ Controlling the amount of enzyme present

Enzymes, like all proteins, are made at the ribosomes and are coded for by genes (see Chapter 4). As we have seen, the rate of a reaction is affected by the concentration of enzyme present. This means that by controlling how much of an enzyme is made, the rate of the reaction it catalyses can be influenced.

This system of control works very well and is used by a number of organisms. For example, if the bacterium *Escherichia coli* is placed on agar containing lactose, it starts producing the enzyme β-galactosidase to break it down. If there is no lactose present in the agar the rate of β-galactosidase production falls. There are problems, however, with this method of control. It is very slow in biochemical terms and gives a rather coarse level of control when what is really needed is fine tuning of the rate of reactions.

■ Switching the enzyme on and off

Certain enzymes can exist in two forms, one active, the other inactive. These forms can be switched from one to the other and so provide a way of controlling how much working enzyme is present at any one time. Such enzymes are known as *allosteric enzymes*.

Allosteric enzymes have at least two binding sites. One site is the active site for the substrate, the other is for an inhibitor molecule. It is thought that when the inhibitor attaches itself to the enzyme, the shape of the latter is changed so that the active site is distorted or masked and the substrate can no longer bind to it. When the inhibitor is released, the enzyme snaps back into its active form (see Fig. 3.17).

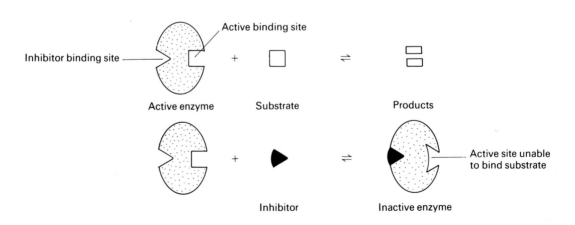

Figure 3.17 Inhibition of an allosteric enzyme.

What sort of molecule can act as an inhibitor? To answer this question, look again at Fig. 3.16. Let's assume that the cell needs a steady supply of N and that N is an inhibitor of the allosteric enzyme y. While N remains at a reasonable level, some of it will be bound to y and so only a certain amount of y will be active, and most of substrate S will go along pathway 1. If for any reason the level of N suddenly falls, less of it will be available to bind to y, more of the enzyme will thus be in the active form and production of N will increase. If N rises above the optimum level, more of it binds to y and production falls. In this way, the level of N or any other chemical whose production is controlled in this way can be regulated to within narrow limits, with very rapid responses to changes in cell conditions.

The enzyme phosphofructokinase (PFK) is an example of an allosteric enzyme. It is involved in the glycolysis stage of respiration. The product of respiration is ATP, which provides the energy for cell activities. However, ATP inhibits PFK, so when the level of ATP is high, the amount of active PFK is low and ATP production falls. If the cell becomes very active, the ATP level falls and more PFK is activated as a result.

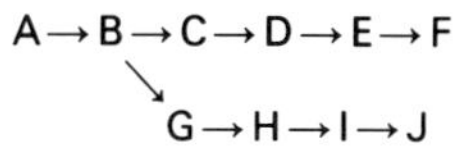

$$A \rightarrow B \rightarrow C \rightarrow D \rightarrow E \rightarrow F$$
$$\searrow$$
$$G \rightarrow H \rightarrow I \rightarrow J$$

Figure 3.18 A branching pathway.

Q Consider the branching pathway in Fig. 3.18. How many allosteric enzymes would you put in for control, and where would it/they be?

Only one would be needed for the junction point, either at

$$B \rightarrow C \quad or \quad B \rightarrow G$$

Where the product of a reaction inhibits its own formation, this is known as *negative feedback*. It is interesting that chemicals other than products can affect allosteric enzymes. PFK, for example, is activated by a chemical called AMP, which can be formed from the breakdown of ATP.

■ APPLICATIONS OF ENZYMES

■ Enzymes in industry

For hundreds of years several industries have been making use of the enzymes locked up in organisms. The brewing industry, for example, relies heavily on diastase and amylase in the barley grain to break down starch into glucose which the enzymes in the brewers yeast, *Saccharomyces cerevisiae*, then convert into alcohol. Cheese production involves the formation of a curd from milk proteins, and the enzyme rennin from calf stomachs is traditionally used for this purpose, although it has mainly been replaced by a protease from bacteria.

The fruit juice industry also makes use of enzymes. When the fruit is pressed, the resulting liquid is cloudy due to the presence of cellular debris, primarily cellulose and pectins from cell walls. Cellulose is insoluble and lies suspended in the juice, while the soluble pectins bind to other molecules to form complexes. This cloudy appearance is acceptable in certain fruit juices, but not in products such as lime juice. Accordingly, cellulases and pectinases (usually obtained from fungi) are added. The cellulose is broken down into glucose; the pectins into sugars and glucuronic acid. As these are soluble the fruit juice clears.

The potential for enzymes in industry is huge. Traditional catalysts are often expensive (e.g. platinum), require the use of high temperatures and/or pressures (which with increasing energy costs are very expensive to provide), and often result in the formation of unwanted by-products which must later be removed at added cost. Enzymes require neither high pressures nor temperatures (quite the opposite, in fact), and are very specific in the reaction they carry out, hence there are fewer un-wanted by-products. At present they are expensive to provide in quantity, but with advances in genetic engineering the price is likely to come down in future. What is more, as enzymes can be immobilised by binding them onto inert substances, there will be no problems in separating them from the final products.

■ Enzymes in medicine

Medicines already exist which contain enzymes in them. Lasonil™, for example is an ointment used for

41

treating bruises, sprains and other swellings. It contains hyaluronidase, an enzyme which acts on hyaluronic acid, a component of the connective tissue substance which helps glue cells together. The effect is to make it easier for the tissues to reabsorb fluid from the affected area and so ease the swelling.

As we've seen in the case of heart attacks, the presence or absence of certain enzymes in the blood can be tested for to confirm a diagnosis. There are other tests, in which enzymes themselves are a component of the technique. Using reagent sticks such as Clinistix™ and Diastix™ to test for glycosuria is a good example. Glycosuria is the presence of glucose in the urine, and is often indicative of diabetes.

The test consists of dipping the stick into a urine sample. If glucose is present, glucose oxidase attached to the stick reacts with it to form gluconic acid and hydrogen peroxide.

$$\text{Glucose} + O_2 + H_2O \xrightarrow[oxidase]{Glucose} \text{gluconic acid} + H_2O_2$$

The peroxide then reacts with a colourless chemical on the stick called a chromogen, which is oxidised to form a coloured product. This is catalysed by a peroxidase.

$$H_2O_2 + \text{chromogen} \xrightarrow{Peroxidase} H_2O_2 + \text{coloured dye}$$

The test is quick (10–30 seconds), easy to perform, specific for glucose and sensitive (it can detect glucose at levels as low as $5-6 \, \text{m mol dm}^{-3}$). It also gives a rough idea as to how much glucose is present, i.e. the more there is, the more peroxide is formed to react with the chromogen and the deeper the colour that results.

A major hope for combating cancer is ADEPT (antibody-directed enzyme prodrug treatment). In this technique, an antibody specific against the tumour cell is linked to an enzyme. Once the antibody-enzyme complex has had time to find its way to the tumour cells and stick to them, the patient is injected with a harmless form of a very toxic drug. The drug stays inactive in the body except at the tumour site, where the enzyme converts it into its toxic form which then kills the cancer cells. Time will tell if this method succeeds (see Fig. 3.19).

■ Enzymes in the home

Any chef will tell you the best way to produce tender pieces of meat; you take the nearest mallet and batter

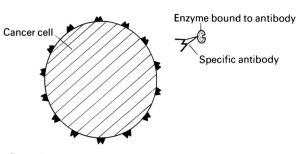

① Antibody and enzyme introduced

② Antibody binds specifically to tumour cell

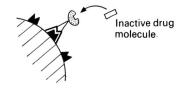

③ Inactive drug introduced

④ Enzyme changes drug to toxic form

⑤ Toxic drug enters cancer cell and kills it

Figure 3.19 How ADEPT works.

it. The idea is to release the enzymes inside the cell lysosomes so that they can act on the tough fibrous tissue and so make the meat easier to chew when cooked. Nowadays tenderising powder is available. This contains papain, an enzyme which breaks down proteins. This has helped to popularise the cheaper cuts of meat. (This explains why fresh fruit may be used when cooking meat, e.g. pineapple with ham. Note that tinned pineapple is ineffective as it has been heated to boiling point.)

Biological washing powders have been available for a number of years. They contain protein digesting enzymes (i.e. proteases) which act on the so-called biological stains such as milk and blood, breaking them down into soluble amino acids which will separate from the fabric. Some of these enzymes were obtained from the bacterium *Bacillus subtilis*, and are known as subtilisins. They are most active at pH 10 and 60°C. Another type of protease works at 37°C and will tolerate a pH of between 7 and 11.5. Some washing powders also have a lipase which will break down fats.

Enzymes are vital in carrying out cell reactions, but how are enzymes themselves made? What determines whether or not an organism can make a particular enzyme? Can an organism learn to make new enzymes?

The answers to these questions can be found in Chapter 4.

■ Box 3.1 CLASSIFICATION OF ENZYMES

As you will have noticed, most enzymes end with the letters -ase. An enzyme's name comes from the type of reaction which it carries out, together with either the substrate it acts upon or the product it forms. For example, the enzyme that removes hydrogen from succinic acid is known as succinic dehydrogenase. There are six main groups of enzymes.

Transferases
These enzymes transfer a chemical group (e.g. amino, methyl) from one substrate to another. For example, the phosphotransferases catalyse the transfer of a phosphate group from one molecule to another.

Hydrolases
These enzymes carry out hydrolysis reactions, i.e. the breaking down of large molecules by the addition of water (see Chapter 2). For example, lipases break down lipids into fatty acids and glycerol.

Ligases
These enzymes form bonds to join two molecules together, using energy supplied from the breakdown of ATP, e.g. DNA ligase is used to repair breaks in DNA molecules.

Oxidoreductases
These enzymes catalyse oxidation reactions, usually involving the transfer of hydrogen from one molecule to another. There are two main types of enzyme:
a) oxidases, where the hydrogen is transferred from a molecule to oxygen, e.g. cytochrome oxidase:

General formula

$$XH_2 + \tfrac{1}{2}O_2 \longrightarrow X + H_2O$$

b) dehydrogenases, where the hydrogen is transferred to a coenzyme such as NAD^+, e.g. succinic dehydrogenase:

General formula

$$XH_2 + NAD^+ \longrightarrow X + NADH/H^+$$

These are very important enzymes in metabolism (see Chapter 1 on respiration).

Isomerases
These enzymes rearrange the atoms in a molecule, e.g. phosphoglucoisomerase:

$$\text{Glucose-6-phosphate} \longrightarrow \text{fructose-6-phosphate}$$

Lyases
These enzymes catalyse the addition of chemical groups to a double bond or the removal of groups to leave a double bond.

CHAPTER 4

DNA - THE MASTER TAPE OF LIFE

■ INTRODUCTION

Sunflowers, sparrows, sticklebacks and sealions. What is it exactly that makes them so different from each other and gives them their individual identity? They are all made up of basically the same types of chemicals, proteins, carbohydrates, lipids, and so on, but put together in a different way. There are differences in the types of reaction which different organisms carry out. But what *makes* the reactions different? Where is the information-carrying blueprint that is followed when charting out the organism's chemical pathways? The answer is found in the intriguing chemical DNA. It is this molecule that carries the coded description of the organism and not only determines which reactions take place, but also ensures that this information is transmitted to the next generation.

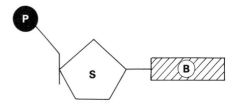

Figure 4.1 A nucleotide, showing the positions of the phosphate, pentose sugar and nitrogenous base.

■ THE NUCLEIC ACIDS

DNA (deoxyribonucleic acid) belongs to a small group of chemicals known as the nucleic acids, so called because they were first identified in cell nuclei. The other nucleic acid is RNA (ribonucleic acid), which as we will see later, exists in several different forms. The nucleic acids are very large molecules. In fact, they are polymers made up of units called nucleotides. Each nucleotide is itself composed of three chemicals joined together, a phosphate, a pentose sugar and a complex nitrogen-containing base (see Fig. 4.1).

Although the phosphate is always the same in every nucleotide, the type of pentose found depends on whether the molecule being looked at is RNA or DNA; in RNA the pentose is a ribose, in DNA it is a deoxyribose (see Fig. 4.2). As you can see, the only difference between the two is the absence of one oxygen atom in the **deoxy**ribose (see Fig. 4.2).

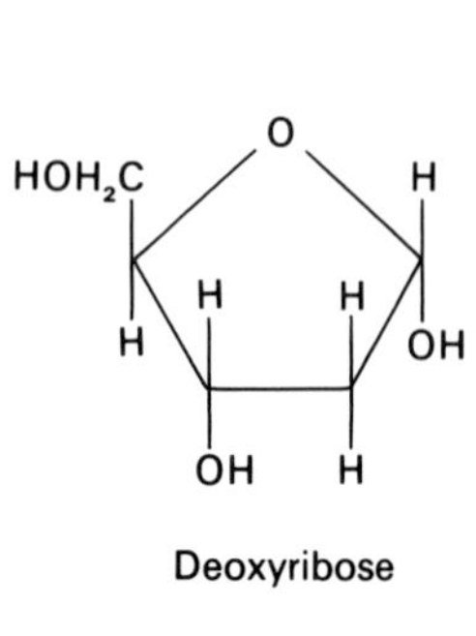

Ribose

Deoxyribose

Figure 4.2 Ribose and deoxyribose.

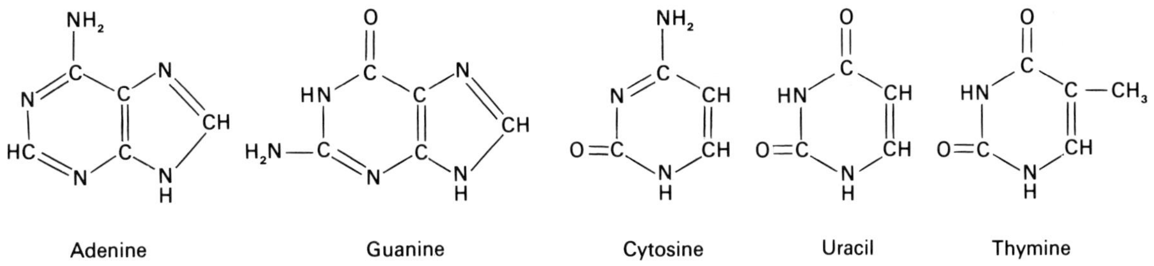

Figure 4.3 The nucleotide bases.

In DNA nucleotides the nitrogenous base can be either a purine (adenine or guanine), or a pyrimidine (cytosine or thymine). Hint: to remember which is which, pyrimidines have a *y* in them (e.g. cytosine), purines don't. RNA has the same bases as DNA, with the exception of thymine, which is replaced by uracil.

Nucleotides are joined together to form a polynucleotide via links between the sugar and phosphate. As you've probably guessed, this is a condensation reaction. The link is called a *phosphodiester* bond.

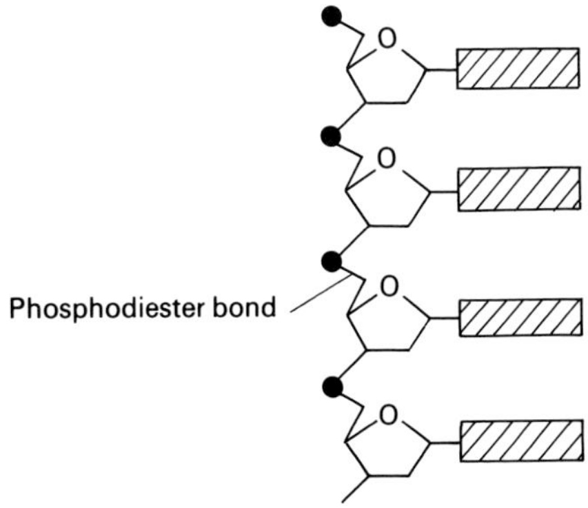

Figure 4.4 Part of a polynucleotide. The key is the same as that shown in Fig. 4.1.

Q Use the available information to draw up a table listing the differences between DNA and RNA.

■ THE STRUCTURE OF DNA

The history of the search for the DNA structure is well known, and provides an excellent example of how pieces of evidence come together from various sources to provide the overall picture.

DNA was first discovered by Miescher in 1869, and extracted from cells found in pus present on the bandages of hospital patients. He called it nuclein. After this it seems to have been regarded as being rather uninteresting until O.T. Avery in 1944 showed that hereditary traits could be transmitted from one bacterial cell to another by purified DNA molecules. Until this time, it was thought that genes, the units that were thought to control biochemical pathways and carry information from one generation to the next, were made of protein. Avery's findings were not accepted by everyone at first, but they certainly stimulated interest in DNA.

The chemical composition of DNA was known by this time, but very little was known about the three-dimensional shape of the molecule. Any model proposed would have to explain two basic features:

● how the DNA carries the coded information for controlling cell metabolism;
● how the DNA produces copies of itself to hand on to the next generation.

Photo 4.1 Watson and Crick.

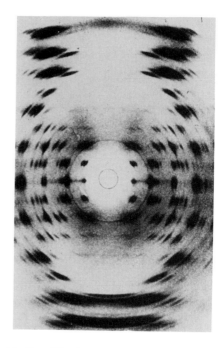

Photo 4.2 X-ray diffraction pattern of DNA ('B' form).

The two names most associated with identifying the structure of DNA are those of James Watson and Francis Crick. Watson had been interested in genes and DNA for some time, and after attending a talk given by Maurice Wilkins in 1951 on the subject he became very excited. Wilkins had shown an X-ray diffraction photograph of DNA, and the very fact that DNA had formed the crystals needed for this process suggested that the molecule had a regular, ordered structure.

Later that year, Watson moved to the Cavendish Laboratories in Cambridge and teamed up with Crick, who shared his interest in the DNA structure.

From the outset, the two scientists assumed that the DNA molecule contained a large number of nucleotides linked together in a regular way to form a chain, with a regular sugar-phosphate backbone. Although the evidence for it was very thin, they favoured a helical shape. Conversations with Wilkins about the X-ray data suggested that the molecule had two, three or four chains.

This left several questions needing to be answered:

- How many chains did the DNA molecule have?
- How were the chains attached to each other?

Watson and Crick decided to try to solve the structure of DNA by building molecular models based on the existing data. In doing so, they had to take into account the findings of Chargaff, who had been chemically analysing DNA since 1949.

Chargaff had discovered that:

1. the base composition of DNA varies from one species to another;

2. the number of adenine residues in DNA is equal to the number of thymine residues (i.e. A = T), and the number of guanine residues is the same as the number of cytosine residues (C = G).

Several models were built, including one with the chain backbones inside a helix, only to be shot down.

The breakthrough came when Rosalind Franklin late in 1952 obtained X-ray photos of DNA to which she had managed to return water molecules – the biologically more important 'B' form.

From this, it was deduced that:

1. the DNA molecule was definitely a helix;

2. the nitrogenous bases were stacked on top of each other at right angles to the helix axis;

3. the diameter of the axis was two nanometres (2×10^{-9} m);

4. the molecule had either two or three chains.

Soon afterwards, Guilland and Jordan produced evidence that suggested that many if not all the bases in DNA formed hydrogen bonds with other bases.

In the first model that Watson built incorporating these new facts, he tried pairing like bases with like, i.e. A with A, T with T, etc.. The result was unsatisfactory, he had used the wrong chemical forms of thymine and guanine to make it fit. He continued to work with cardboard cut-outs of the bases, however, and soon realised that when adenine was paired with thymine, the overall shape of the two molecules was identical to a cytosine-guanine pairing. What's more, the pairings were stably held together by hydrogen bonds (see Figs. 4.5 and 4.6).

Q Look back again at Chargaff's work. Can you see its significance?

The final model was a right-handed helix of two chains, with their phosphate-sugar backbones running in opposite directions. The bases were lying inside the helix, stacked on top of each other and lying at right-angles to the backbone. The chains were held together by hydrogen bonds between the bases, adenine always pairing with thymine, cytosine with guanine (the base sequence of one chain, in fact, automatically determined the base sequence of the other). It was in 1953 that Watson and Crick first published in *Nature* the paper that started 'We wish to suggest a structure ...' Not only did their model

conform with all the evidence available, it also immediately suggested a mechanism by which the genes were copied. Watson, Crick and Wilkins were awarded the Nobel Prize for medicine in 1962.

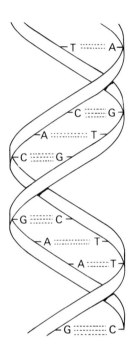

Figure 4.6 DNA structure (note the hydrogen bonding between A and T, and between G and C).

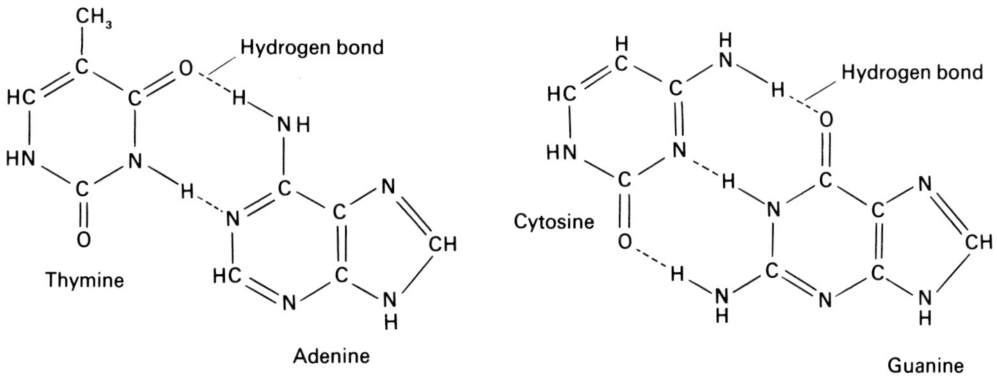

Figure 4.5 A-T and C-G pairings. A is said to be complementary to T and G complementary to C.

■ REPLICATION OF DNA

When cells divide, each daughter cell must obviously receive a copy of the genetic material. In addition, the copy has got to be an accurate one. The double helix model of the DNA molecule lends itself very nicely to this process. What happens is that the DNA molecule is progressively unwound by an enzyme, just like undoing a zip, to leave two chains with unpaired bases. Each chain then acts as a guiding base, or template, for the building up of a new strand alongside it (see Fig. 4.7).

Remember that adenine will only hydrogen-bond with thymine, and cytosine with guanine, so that if a T is present on the old strand only A can lie alongside it in the new strand, and so on. As the appropriate nucleotide is brought into place, it is joined to the growing chain by an enzyme called *DNA polymerase III*. The final result is two DNA molecules, each made up of one newly synthesised chain and one chain that has been conserved from the original molecule; hence the name given to the process of *semi-*

conservative replication. Because of the specific nature of the base pairing, each new molecule has exactly the same base sequence as the original.

Just because a hypothesis seems to be the obvious answer to a problem doesn't mean that it is right. As with all other proposals, supporting evidence is needed. Evidence for the semi-conservative model of replication was provided by Meselson and Stahl working with the bacterium *Escherichia coli*.

They grew *E. coli* in a medium in which the only source of nitrogen to make purines, etc. was of the so-called 'heavy' variety, i.e. the ^{15}N isotope. As a result, all the bases in the DNA contained ^{15}N. They then switched the bacteria to a medium which contained only 'light' nitrogen, i.e. the normal ^{14}N isotope, and allowed them to reproduce once. When the DNA from this generation was isolated, it was found to have a density halfway between that of the DNA taken from the bacteria grown on a light ^{14}N medium and that of the original parents with heavy ^{15}N DNA (see Fig. 4.8).

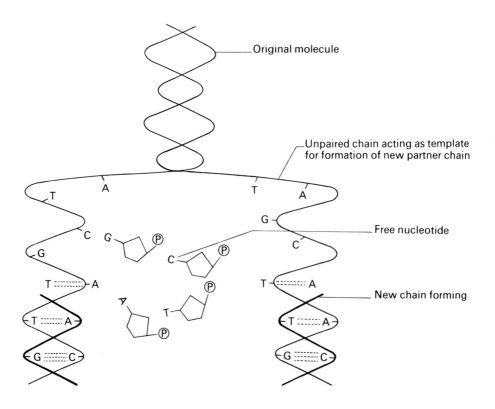

Figure 4.7 Semi-conservative replication.

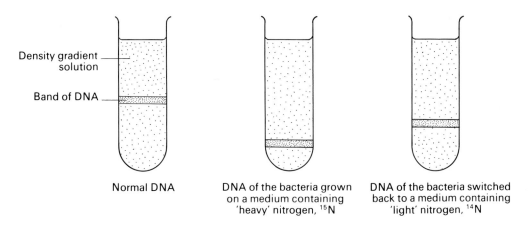

Figure 4.8 Results of Meselson and Stahl's experiment.

Density gradient solution

Band of DNA

Normal DNA

DNA of the bacteria grown on a medium containing 'heavy' nitrogen, ^{15}N

DNA of the bacteria switched back to a medium containing 'light' nitrogen, ^{14}N

Q *Stop and think* for a few moments. What would be your explanation of these results in terms of the DNA replication?

As the original bacteria only had heavy ^{15}N available, all of their DNA bases had this isomer in them. They were then switched to the light ^{14}N medium. When they reproduced and the DNA had to replicate, the bases in the new chain had ^{14}N, i.e. the new DNA molecules had one light and one heavy chain. This would mean that in a density gradient this DNA would appear halfway between normal DNA with two light chains and the DNA of bacteria grown on the ^{15}N medium with two heavy chains. This provided strong evidence for the semi-conservative hypothesis and indirectly supported the double helix model. Incidentally, Meselson and Stahl took their experiment through several generations of bacteria, using the semi-conservative hypothesis to correctly predict the proportion of heavy, light and medium DNA bands that they would obtain in each generation.

■ PROTEIN SYNTHESIS

At the start of this chapter, we emphasised that the DNA carries the coded description of the organism. Amongst other things, this code determines which reactions can take place within the organism. How does this occur? Quite simply, each code carried on a particular length of DNA (called a *gene*) determines the sequence in which various amino acids are joined together to form a particular polypeptide chain. In a nutshell, DNA controls protein synthesis.

You will recall that all enzymes are proteins (see Chapter 3). You will also remember that enzymes control all reactions, i.e. if you haven't got an enzyme for a reaction, the activation energy needed will be too high for the reaction to occur. As the DNA determines which enzymes are made and therefore which reactions occur, it will determine the nature of the organism's metabolism and thus the nature of the organism itself.

It is possible to separate molecules of different masses by using a technique known as *density gradient centrifugation*. The molecules are placed in an ultracentrifuge (i.e. a centrifuge which can generate a high *g* force) on top of a caesium chloride solution. As the centrifuge spins the caesium chloride partially sediments to form a density gradient, with the density becoming greater towards the end of the tube. The molecules which are added to the tube will separate out, with the 'heavier' molecules travelling further down the tube.

gene a specific length of a DNA molecule made up of a sequence of nucleotides, to which a specific function can be assigned.

■ THE GENETIC CODE

It is interesting to consider at this point how the DNA molecule can possibly contain a code capable of providing the information required to synthesise a wide variety of proteins. The sugar and phosphate components of the nucleotides can't be involved, as these just alternate regularly down the chain. There is only one component (i.e. the bases) that changes, and so it must be the sequence of bases in the DNA chain that codes for the sequence of amino acids in the polypeptide.

Somehow, twenty different amino acids are coded for by only four types of base. Obviously, the system does not involve one base = one amino acid, as this would only allow for proteins with four types of amino acid in them. Similarly a code made up of a sequence of two bases on the chain would only allow for sixteen amino acids. Therefore, at least three bases are needed to specify each amino acid. A 'triplet code' gives sixty-four possible combinations, more than enough for the twenty amino acids commonly found in proteins. Each triplet is known as a *codon*.

It wasn't until the early 1960s that the code itself was completely cracked. From all the work done to date it seems that the code is universal for all forms of life from bacteria to humans.

You will see from Table 4.1 that most of the amino acids have more than one triplet coding for them, so the code is said to be *degenerate*. This doesn't matter, as any of the six different codons for serine, for example, will result in serine appearing in the right place.

Notice that the base uracil appears in the genetic code. The reason for this will become clear later, as will the presence of three codons which don't code for any amino acid.

■ THE PROCESS

As you know, the DNA is found in the nucleus as part of the chromosomes. The organelles that *make* the proteins, however, are the ribosomes, and these are found either fixed to endoplasmic reticulum or free in the cytoplasm (see Fig. 1.5). It is like keeping the blueprints to make a piece of machinery in London whilst the factory doing the job is in Cardiff. The process must first involve copying the blueprint, sending it from one place to the other, then reading it at the other end to make the final product. This is exactly what happens in protein synthesis. The copying of the genetic code carried on the gene is known as *transcription*, while the formation of a polypeptide chain at the ribosomes using the code is called *translation*.

UUU	Phe	UCU	Ser	UAU	Tyr	UGU	Cys
UUC	Phe	UCC	Ser	UAC	Tyr	UGC	Cys
UUA	Leu	UCA	Ser	UAA	Terminator	UGA	Terminator
UUG	Leu	UCG	Ser	UAA	Terminator	UGG	Trp
CUU	Leu	CCU	Pro	CAU	His	CGU	Arg
CUC	Leu	CCC	Pro	CAC	His	CGC	Arg
CUA	Leu	CCA	Pro	CAA	Gln	CGA	Arg
CUG	Leu	CCG	Pro	CAG	Gln	CGG	Arg
AUU	Ile	ACU	Thr	AAU	Asn	AGU	Ser
AUC	Ile	ACC	Thr	AAC	Asn	AGC	Ser
AUA	Ile	ACA	Thr	AAA	Lys	AGA	Arg
AUG	Met	ACG	Thr	AAG	Lys	AGG	Arg
GUU	Val	GCU	Ala	GAU	Asp	GGU	Gly
GUC	Val	GCC	Ala	GAC	Asp	GGC	Gly
GUA	Val	GCA	Ala	GAA	Glu	GGA	Gly
GUG	Val	GCG	Ala	GAG	Glu	GGG	Gly

Table 4.1 The genetic code, i.e. the meaning of mRNA codons.

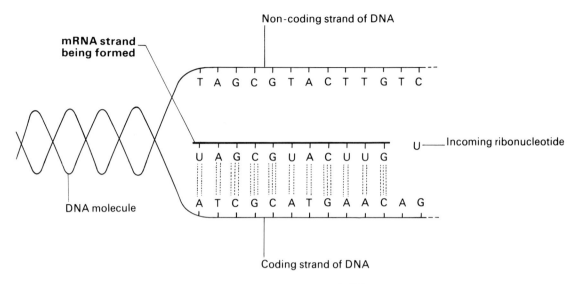

Figure 4.9 Transcription. Note that the codons in mRNA are complementary to those in DNA. Descriptions of the genetic code are usually given in terms of mRNA (see Table 4.1).

■ Transcription

This stage involves unzipping the double helix and using one of the strands as a template to synthesise the copy molecule. The copy however uses uracil instead of thymine, and the sugar ribose instead of deoxyribose, i.e. the copy is a molecule of RNA, known appropriately as *messenger RNA* (mRNA).

An enzyme (RNA polymerase) plays a major part in transcription. The process begins at a particular location on the DNA molecule known as the promoter region. This always contains the base sequence ATATTAC or some variation of this sequence and acts as a 'start here' signal to the polymerase. The enzyme begins work a few bases further on by separating the two chains from each other. One chain then acts as the template. Free nucleotides present in the nucleoplasm hydrogen bond to their appropriate partner on the template chain, and the RNA polymerase binds them together to form a chain. The messenger RNA molecule formed has a base sequence complementary to that of the template DNA strand (see Fig. 4.9). The mRNA now leaves the nucleus and enters the cytoplasm carrying the codons that specify the amino acid sequence of a future protein.

■ Translation

Once the mRNA is in the cytoplasm, ribosomes bind to it. Ribosomes are small organelles which have two subunits, each made up of protein and another type of RNA, ribosomal RNA (rRNA).

The prime objective of the ribosomes is to translate the sequence of codons carried on the mRNA into the sequence of amino acids which will form the polypeptide chain. However, there is a problem. The amino acids and codons are so dissimilar in structure that there is no way in which a particular amino acid can just fit alongside the appropriate codon. Instead, a molecular adaptor is needed, one that can bind to a particular codon at one end and the amino acid which that codon codes for at the other end. Such adaptors exist and they are all types of a third form of RNA known as *transfer RNA (tRNA)*. Each amino acid has its own tRNA molecule. Indeed, some amino acids have more than one.

A tRNA molecule looks vaguely like a clover leaf with its three loops. At one end, which always has the base sequence ACC, is the binding site for the amino acid. It is very specific and only allows one particular type of amino acid to attach itself. On the

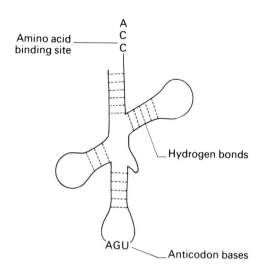

Figure 4.10 A tRNA molecule. The anticodon bases vary.

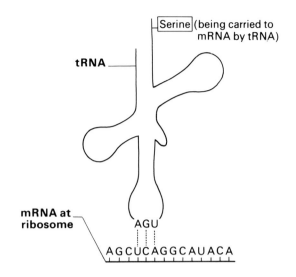

Figure 4.11 Codon-anticodon binding.

bottom loop there is a sequence of three unpaired bases, the *anticodon* (see Fig. 4.10).

Let's take an example to see how it works. The codon UCA on the mRNA codes for the amino acid serine. Present in the cytoplasm will be a tRNA molecule with the complementary sequence to these bases, i.e. the anticodon AGU. The tRNA will link only to serine at its amino acid binding site. The amino acid needs activating before it will link to the tRNA, and the energy for this comes from a molecule of ATP. Once formed, the serine-tRNA complex moves towards the mRNA and hydrogen bonds to the codon, effectively holding the serine in position (see Fig. 4.11). Now that all the ingredients are present, how does the actual process of stitching together the amino acids take place?

The ribosome binds at one end of the mRNA molecule. All the ingredients required to make the polypeptide chain are brought close together in the ribosome. On the ribosome there are three binding sites; one for the mRNA molecule on the small sub-unit (see Fig. 4.12(a)), and one for each tRNA/amino acid complex. When all three components are present, the amino acids are located in the ideal position to form a peptide bond between them. Bonding occurs and the ribosome then moves on to the next tRNA in line, forms a bond between its amino acid and the previous one, moves on, forms a bond, moves on, and so on. In this way a chain of amino acids is readily produced. As each amino acid

is incorporated into the chain its tRNA is released. This tRNA is then free to combine with another amino acid and bring it to the mRNA. When the ribosome reaches the end of the mRNA chain, it is set free and the completed polypeptide chain is released.

However, the polypeptide chain is not yet a working protein. It must be folded into the right shape, have any disulphide bridges formed and possibly be joined on to other polypeptide chains. When all of these post-translational modifications have been carried out, the protein is ready either for use within the cell or for secretion via the Golgi body (see Fig. 1.5).

How does the ribosome determine where to begin and end the process of translation? Although you may think this is a simple process, some mRNAs have the coding sequence for several polypeptide chains all fitted together, end to end, in the same molecule. The answer lies in the codons carried by the mRNA. When the codon AUG (the code for methionine) is encountered, translation begins. However, not every protein begins with methionine. In most cases the methionine is cut off the polypeptide chain once the process has finished. Translation is finished when the ribosome reaches one of the codons that doesn't code for an amino acid (i.e. UGA, UAA or UAG). These codons act as stop signals. To speed up production, more than one ribosome may be involved with a single mRNA molecule, thus forming a complex known as a *polysome*.

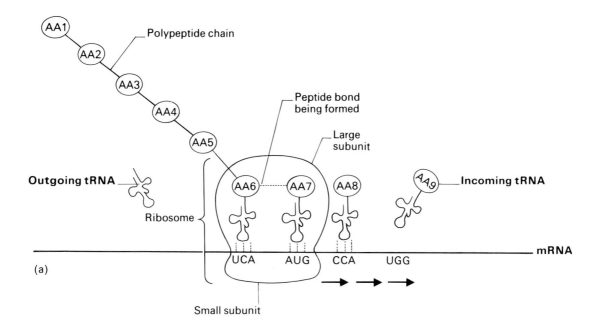

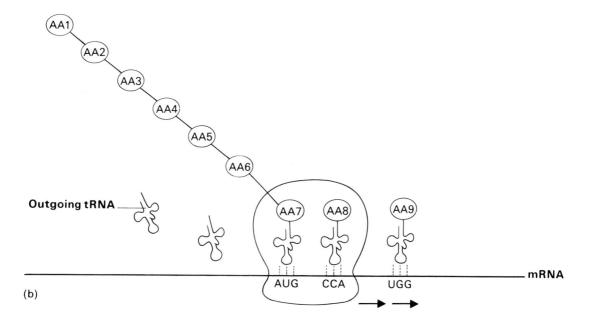

Figure 4.12   Synthesis of the polypeptide chain. How the ribosome can tell the difference between a 'start here' AUG codon and an AUG codon in the middle of the chain is, alas, outside the scope of this book. Suffice it to say that it can.

■ DNA PROFILING

DNA profiling, or genetic fingerprinting, is the name given to a technique that can identify an individual with certainty from a sample of the individual's genetic material. Alec Jeffreys at Leicester University found that human DNA contains particular base sequences that are repeated many times. The length of each repeated sequence, the number of repeats and their exact location within the molecule are unique to a particular individual. These sequences, or minisatellites, can be made visible by the use of DNA probes. By labelling the DNA probe with radioactive ^{32}P isotope, mixing the probe with an individual's DNA and exposing the mixture to photographic film, the minisatellite positions can be identified.

The result (see photo), which looks something like a supermarket bar code, differs in appearance between every individual (except for identical twins, who have exactly the same genetic material).

There are various applications for such a technique, for example when proving the presence of a person at the scene of a crime. DNA profiling can also be used to establish whether or not a man is the father of a child in a paternity case. As you know, we inherit half our DNA from each of our parents. This means that in a DNA profile, half of the bands will have come from the father and half from the mother. By comparing DNA profiles from the mother, the child and the alleged father, paternity can be effectively confirmed or disproved.

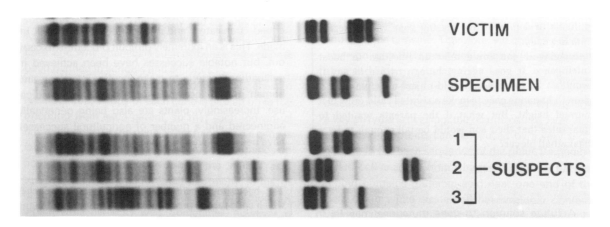

Photo 4.3   DNA profiles of a victim, a specimen (of blood, semen, etc) obtained from the scene of the crime, and several suspects. Can you identify the villain?

THE NUTRITION OF HETEROTROPHS: A BIOCHEMICAL VIEWPOINT

CHAPTER 5

■ INTRODUCTION

Growth requires both *energy* in the form of ATP and *materials*. In this chapter and the next we shall explore both the obtaining and using of materials and energy. Logically we should start with plants. In a science fiction novel by the astronomer Fred Hoyle, an alien life form reasons that the surprising success of animal life on the planet Earth is due to *'the development of an entirely new type of plant, the plant you call grass.'*

This observation may well be correct. The life of the entire planet depends upon the capture of solar energy by plant chlorophyll and the channelling of that captured energy through the plants and then up through the various kinds of food chains. As discussed in Chapter 1, plants use some of the organic compounds that they make by photosynthesis as their own oxidisable fuel. Many of these compounds, however, are available to the *grazing food chain* (for herbivores such as birds and for the carnivores that eat them) and to the *decomposer food chain* (for scavengers, fungi and bacteria in the soil). Figure 5.1 shows a simple example of a food and energy chain.

Despite the fact that plants are the primary producers (or *autotrophs*) and are gatherers of solar energy and makers of organic compounds, this chapter and the next will focus on the nutrition and metabolism of *heterotrophs*. These organisms need to have an intake of complex nutrients.

There are several reasons for dealing first with heterotrophs and in particular with animals. One reason is that in some respects plants are more complicated: they possess not only all the enzymes necessary for the catabolic reactions of respiration but also all the enzymes of photosynthesis. In contrast, animals respire but do not photosynthesise and, therefore, make an easier starting point.

A second reason is that, historically, the major catabolic pathways such as glycolysis and the Krebs cycle, were discovered mainly in experiments on the tissue of heterotrophs. In the 1920s and 1930s, early work on glycolysis centred mainly on yeast cells. Later, in the 1930s and 1940s, Albert Szent-Gyorgyi and Hans Krebs made huge advances in the study of catabolism using preparations of rat liver and minced pigeon-breast muscle.

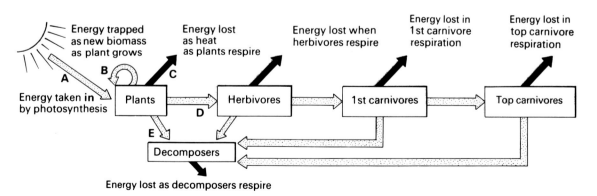

Figure 5.1   A food and energy chain. Note that as the law of conservation of energy *must* apply, i.e. energy A (kJ) = B + C + D + E. Note also that all organisms respire, usually using O_2 to give CO_2 and H_2O and lost energy.

Photo 5.1 Hans Krebs.

Getting compounds from the external environment into the true interior of an organism is termed *assimilation*. In the distant past, the simplest unicellular heterotrophs would have simply absorbed organic compounds present in the water around them, perhaps after secreting a few hydrolytic enzymes into the water to digest some of the larger molecules. As evolution continued and multicellular organisms evolved, there gradually came into being a host of different methods of 'capturing' the environmental organic compounds, digesting them, absorbing them and transporting them to all parts of the organism.

There are numerous fascinating examples of the different methods of heterotrophic feeding, and how each is related to the organism's environment: a tapeworm absorbing nutrients from the gut, a limpet slowly browsing over shore-line rocks rasping off the film of seaweed much as a cow crops grass, a tiny aphid pushing its tubular proboscis down into the sugar-containing phloem of plants, fungi invading and rotting both living and dead tissue, bacteria living on skin, faeces, leaf litter, teeth or crude oil.

But as biochemists, we are concerned with features of these feeding methods that are common to all heterotrophs.

● What chemicals do heterotrophs need to obtain in their *diet*?

● How are the compounds of each diet converted into a form that can be taken into the cells of the organism. (What is the biochemistry of *digestion*?)

● How are the products of digestion moved from the exterior to the interior of an organism. In this context, the lumen (interior space) of the intestine is *outside* the body. (What is the biochemistry of *absorption*?)

● Leaving aside the physiological processes by which absorbed compounds are transported to tissues, how do these compounds enter cells and how are they used by the organism in *catabolism and anabolism*?

■ HETEROTROPHIC DIETS: AN OVERVIEW

Memories of earlier biology courses will, probably, bring to the front of your mind the idea that *proteins, carbohydrates* and *fats* along with other odds and ends such as *minerals, vitamins, essential amino acids* and *essential fatty acids* are important. And so they are if we are talking, for example, about ourselves or other mammals. We, as true heterotrophs, depend on pre-formed organic compounds to a very great extent. Not only must all of our carbon come in organic form but so also must all of our nitrogen and sulphur. A quick spoonful of sulphate ion contributes nothing to us nutritionally and the nitrate ion is not our source of nutritional nitrogen. In fact, the nitrate ion is slightly toxic (hence all the concern about high nitrate levels in drinking water).

In contrast to animals, many other heterotrophs have few dietary demands. For example, though the gut bacterium *E. coli* requires an organic source of carbon (i.e. glucose), it can normally manage perfectly well with an inorganic source for nitrogen and sulphur. Table 5.1 shows the composition of a typical laboratory growth medium for *E. coli*.

These dietary differences between heterotrophs, e.g. between ourselves and cats, between mushrooms and bacteria, are simply a reflection of what kind of enzymes each different species possesses. And that in turn determines which genes and hence which enzymes will be gained or lost by the different species during evolution.

The 'rules' about heterotrophic nutrition are simple:

● heterotrophs *always* use organic carbon;

● heterotrophs *must* obtain from their food all other elements necessary to make the complete range of cell chemicals. Sometimes these will be assimilated as organic compounds and sometimes as inorganic compounds;

● any organic compound that the cells of a heterotroph need but cannot make *must* be obtained ready-made in the diet (e.g. vitamins).

These general points are summarised in Fig. 5.2.

Constituent	Quantity
Water	1 dm³
Glucose	5 g
Ammonium chloride	1 g
Potassium hydrogen phosphate	1 g
Magnesium sulphate	0.2 g
Iron (II) sulphate	0.01 g
Calcium Chloride	0.01 g
Mn, Mo, Cu, Co, Zn (as ions)	0.02–0.05 mg each

Table 5.1 Suitable growth medium for *Escherichia coli*.

■ HUMAN DIET

Figure 5.2 reminds you of an important point introduced in Chapter 1, i.e. the diet has to supply both *energy* and *materials* for growth and maintenance. Let's consider these in turn in relation to the human diet.

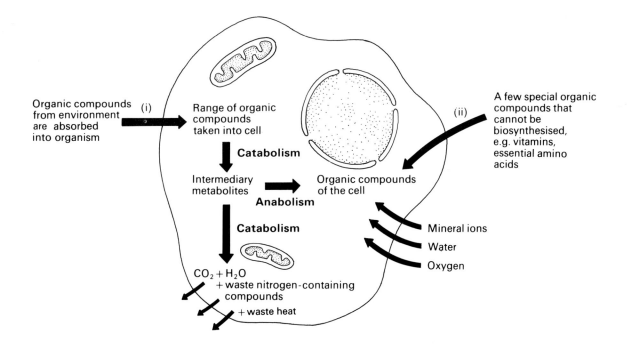

Figure 5.2 Diet in eukaryotic heterotrophs. All C, N and S, most (organic) H and O and some P enter by route (i). Organic compounds that the cell needs, but cannot make for itself, account for route (ii). Note especially that the range of organic compounds transported across the plasma membrane provides the cell with fuel to catabolise and small organic compounds with which to build cell chemicals by anabolism.

■ Energy supply

As far as energy requirements are concerned, we catabolise a mixture of proteins, fats and carbohydrates to provide the ATP that we need. The various ways in which these compounds are broken down, i.e. catabolised, *in vivo* are described in Chapter 6.

In terms of energy alone, i.e. leaving aside the question of materials for biosynthesis, our daily energy need in kilojoules could be supplied by eating nothing but carbohydrates, or nothing but fat, or nothing but protein, or any mixture of the three. What a person actually eats is influenced by taste, wealth and culture. In the West, an average diet is such that about 50% of the daily energy requirement is obtained from carbohydrate, 35% from fat and 15% from protein.

The number of **kilojoules** required per day depends, among other things, on body size, activity, and age, and these are, of course interrelated factors. The underlying principle that determines what a person needs is the law of conservation of energy. If body mass is to be constant, the number of kilojoules *in* (as food) must exactly equal the number of kilojoules *out* (as heat and work done on other objects).

For many people this balance of energy is achieved easily and usually without any conscious thought. For others, the effort of restraining themselves from eating is a constant battle, with the person's obesity showing the extent to which they fail. It has been calculated that just two butter pats per day in excess of what is needed for a balanced diet leads to a weight increase over the year of around 5 kg. The only way to start *losing weight*, if you need to, is either to increase energy loss (i.e. exercise) or to decrease input (i.e. diet).

A young, moderately active, adult male, weighing 70 kg, requires approximately 10 000 kJ per day. Anything in excess of this is stored initially as glycogen in the liver and muscle and, if there is a large excess, as fat droplets in the fat cells (adipocytes).

The glycogen store is very much short term. It is the first to be laid down and the first to be used up when food is not taken: all stored glycogen is used up within 24 hours. Longer starvation leads to a progressive depletion of the fat reserves (of which there are 12 kg or more). There are no protein reserves as such, but in prolonged starvation muscle protein is progressively and dangerously lost. Prisoners taking water but no food during hunger strikes have died after about 60 days.

■ MATERIALS

A sufficient number of kilojoules is one dietary consideration, but the supply of the building blocks of anabolism and other metabolic essentials is another. Consider the various components of the normal diet one by one.

■ Proteins

What of dietary protein requirement? How much do we need in our diet? Why do we need protein at all? *In vivo*, proteins perform essential tasks which were discussed in Chapter 2. However, proteins are being continuously broken down; first to amino acids and then by *deamination* of the amino acids in the liver to carbon dioxide water and urea. Figure 5.3 shows this process in more detail.

Because of this continuous loss of protein they must be replaced in the diet. And, because what we eat are plants and other animals, the replacement is in the form of 'polymerised amino acids', namely protein. It is important, however, that the mixture of dietary proteins contains an *adequate amount of all twenty amino acids*; around 60 g per day is sufficient. How wasteful and over-indulgent it must seem then when, in Europe or the USA, we may eat a half pound steak, eggs, peas, muesli, bacon and all in one day!

Kilojoules modern biology uses joules and kilojoules. Dieticians, however, may still use the term calories. (Often a kilocalorie is called a Calorie, with a capital 'C'). One kilojoule is equal to 4.2 kilocalories. A requirement of 10 000 kJ per day, therefore, is equal to 10 000 ÷ 4.2, i.e. 2381 kilocalories (or Calories) per day.

losing weight this is not *quite* true. If you increase your basal metabolic rate (BMR), you will convert food to energy without apparently doing exercise. Programmes of regular exercise usually lead to a higher BMR, thus the weight-reducing value of exercise is enhanced.

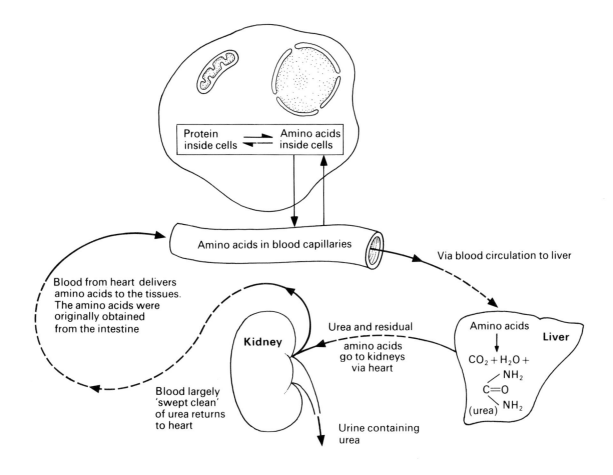

Figure 5.3 The dynamic equilibrium of proteins is the term applied to the opposing reaction shown in the panel in the cell. Breakdown is brought about by intracellular proteases. Synthesis is a complex process described in Chapter 4. Urea is produced in the liver by a pathway called the urea cycle. Note that aquatic organisms produce ammonia instead of urea, birds produce uric acid (bird lime) instead of urea.

What of vegetarians? Can they remain healthy on plant proteins many of which are deficient in one or more particular amino acids? Adult humans are unable to synthesise the carbon skeleton of some eight of the twenty amino acids, yet those amino acids are essential components of essential proteins (see Table 5.2). For example, lysine and methionine are present in haemoglobin, yet we can synthesise neither amino acid. For this reason, all those amino acids shown in Table 5.2 must be obtained in our food and hence are called the *essential amino acids*. Protein from other animals is normally an excellent source of these essential amino acids and milk protein contains the whole range. Plant proteins, however, are sometimes deficient (or almost totally

lacking) in one or more of the essential amino acids. For example, maize has almost no lysine and beans are very deficient in methionine. For this reason, vegetarians, especially vegans who eat no animal products, are at some risk of having an inadequate intake of certain amino acids. Fortunately, by having the right mix of plant protein, e.g. maize plus beans in this example, the problem of amino acid deficiency can be avoided.

Besides needing dietary amino acids for protein synthesis, they are also the principal sources of nitrogen for other compounds, DNA, RNA, ATP, NAD^+, $NADP^+$, to name but a few! The amino acids methionine, cysteine and cystine are also a source of sulphur.

Non-essential	Essential
Alanine	Arginine
Asparagine	Histidine
Aspartate	Isoleucine
Cysteine	Leucine
Glutamate	Lysine
Glutamine	Methionine
Glycine	Phenylalanine
Proline	Threonine
Serine	Tryptophan
Tyrosine	Valine

Table 5.2 Of the twenty amino acids coded by the genetic code, ten of these must be supplied in the diet of a growing child. In an adult arginine and histidine cease to be essential as they are made at a very slow rate in the body.

■ Carbohydrates and fats

Considering fats and carbohydrates, (especially carbohydrate in the form of sugar) medical controversy over the dietary requirements of these components continues unabated! Both are excellent (and cheap) sources of energy but both may have uncertain effects (see Chapter 2).

■ Vitamins and minerals

Finally we must consider the quantitatively lesser but nevertheless essential dietary components, the vitamins and minerals. Regarding the minerals, refer again to Table 1.1. The involvement of the various minerals in bone and teeth is vital but will not be discussed here. Pay particular attention instead to the involvement of (a) metals as essential, covalently-bound components of the *prosthetic* (i.e. non-protein) groups of enzymes and other proteins and (b) of metal ions as activators of certain enzymes. This was discussed in some detail in Chapter 3 and Table 5.3 provides a summary.

Vitamins are organic compounds required in very small quantities in the diet. Though this definition is similar to that of the essential amino acids, the latter are required daily in gram quantities whereas vitamins are needed in milligram or microgram quantities. The list of vitamins differs somewhat from species to species. Table 5.4 shows those that we require. Box 5.1 describes how some of the B-group vitamins are involved in the structure of coenzymes. (Note the details about NAD^+, $NADP^+$ and FAD which are important in later chapters.)

Enzyme name	Metal	Comment
Hexokinase (HK)	Magnesium	Mg^{2+} ions are not tightly bound to the protein: they assist ATP binding.
Phosphofructokinase (PFK)	Magnesium	See Chapter 6 for more details of HK and PFK
Alcohol dehydrogenase	Zinc	The zinc prosthetic group is essential in its catalytic role of forming/catabolising ethanol
Catalase	Iron	The iron is part of a haem prosthetic group (as in haemoglobin).
Nitrogenase	Iron and molybdenum	The metal ions are tightly bound to the protein in this crucially important enzyme that converts N_2 to NH_3 in nitrogen fixation
Isocitric dehydrogenase (ICDH)	Manganese	This is one enzyme of the Krebs cycle

Table 5.3 Some metals in enzymes.

In later chapters, you will find that many important reactions in both the catabolic and anabolic pathways involve reactions in which the coenzymes NAD^+, $NADP^+$, and FAD are involved. You will also hear a good deal about an activated form of ethanoic acid which, based on the old-fashioned name 'acetic acid' for ethanoic acid, biochemists call *acetyl co-enzyme A*. All these coenzymes are formed from one or other of the B-group vitamins.

Consider the coenzyme NAD^+ (nicotinamide adenine dinucleotide). The name tells us that the structure contains nicotinamide, i.e. vitamin B_3. Look at Figure 1 below. Although the formulae shown here are not ones to be remembered, it is useful to look at them to see how the important hydrogen-carrying coenzyme works in molecular terms. It also explains the origin of the plus sign in the abbreviated equation. (This equation, where XH_2 is a substance that needs dehydrogenating, is much used later on in the book.)

As *none* of the catabolic pathways by which we make ATP from our ingested fuels will work without NAD^+, and as we are completely unable to make nicotinamide, the status of niacin as a vitamin in our diet is very evident.

Much the same type of story applies to $NADP^+$ (nicotinamide adenine dinucleotide phosphate).

This is also made from nicotinamide; indeed the only difference is an extra phosphate group. FAD (flavin adenine dinucleotide) has a structure that contains riboflavin, and coenzyme A has a complex structure that contains pantothenic acid. The detailed structures of these coenzymes do not matter. However, you should know that FAD is another hydrogen carrier and works, in simple terms, as follows:

$$FAD + XH_2 \longrightarrow X + FADH_2$$

Pantothenic acid contains an —SH group; this is very similar to the —OH group you are familiar with except the oxygen is replaced with sulphur. Even when bundled up into the structure of coenzyme A, the —SH group is still present and is very important. Thus the abbreviation for coenzyme A is usually written CoASH, and we show its reaction with ethanoic acid (acetic acid) as follows:

$$CH_3.COOH + CoA—SH \rightarrow CH_3.CO—S—CoA + H_2O$$
Acetic acid   Coenzyme A   Acetyl CoA   Water

The resulting product acetyl CoA is an important molecule in catabolism and will be discussed in more detail later on.

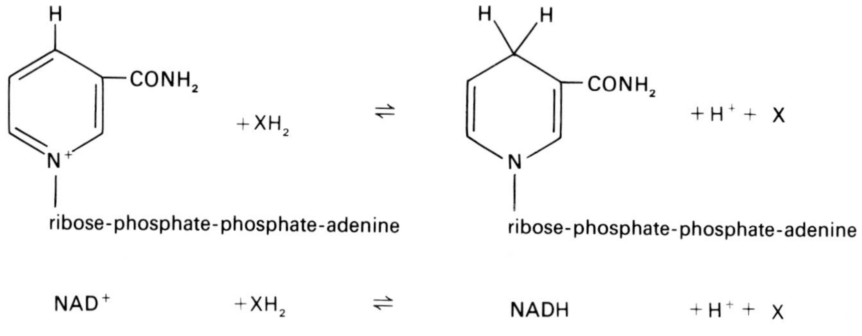

Figure 1

Vitamin	Role
Fat soluble vitamins	
A (retinol)	This polyunsaturated alcohol is converted to the light-sensitive pigment in the retina of the eye
D (calciferol)	This vitamin can be made from cholesterol in the skin in sunlight. However, extra is needed in the diet. It is important in calcium and phosphorus metabolism – hence in bone formation
E (α-tocopherol)	This vitamin somehow protects the lipids of membranes from becoming oxidised
K (phylloquinone)	This vitamin is important in the mechanism of blood clotting
Water-soluble vitamins	
C (ascorbic acid)	Vitamin C is essential in the production of collagen – the protein of connective tissue.
B-group vitamins Thiamin (B_1) Riboflavin (B_2) Niacin Pantothenic acid (B_5) Pyridoxine (B_6) Cobalamin (B_{12}) Folic acid (M) Biotin (H)	All of these water soluble enzymes are part of what is loosely called the B-group of vitamins. Mostly the chemical names are used now. The distinguishing feature of the B-group vitamins is that they all play a part in the structure of various coenzymes. See Box 5.1.

Table 5.4   Fat-soluble and water-soluble vitamins.

■ DIGESTION

We now know which organic compounds hetero-trophs ingest. But, by what process are these often very large molecules consumed and converted into a form in which they can pass through the plasma membrane?

Q From what you have read already and from your general biological knowledge, can you give the name of the process, say on what kind of chemical reaction it is based and, finally, list the major examples?

The process is, of course, digestion and the reaction common to the digestion of all compounds in all organisms is that of *hydrolysis*. The hydrolysable compounds of food, i.e. proteins, polysaccharides, disaccharides and fats, are all split, through the action of water, into their component parts. These, being much smaller molecules, are then readily absorbed across membranes into the true interior of the organism. The digestive enzymes and their reac-tions are shown in Table 5.5. You should be able to understand this table using your knowledge from Chapter 2. Look at columns 1 to 3 of Table 5.5 and make sure that the conversions are familiar to you.

None of these hydrolytic reactions occurs at any noticeable rate at room temperature. Mix starch, fat and protein with water and they remain almost un-changed. Indeed, it is just as well they do otherwise we would see the wool of sheep dissolve in a shower of rain. To make the hydrolytic reactions of digestion go at the desired rate, a sizeable number of different hydrolytic enzymes (i.e. *hydrolases*) are produced by the organism in question.

Energy is neither required nor released in the digestive process except to the small extent that makes the hydrolytic reactions thermodynamically possible. All that is happening in energetic terms is that the large-moleculed insoluble fuel of steak and chips is being converted to the small-moleculed soluble fuel, i.e. the mixture of amino acids, glucose, glycerol and fatty acids, which are present in the duodenum.

64

Enzyme name	Substrate	Reaction	Comment
Amylase	Starch, glycogen	Glu-Glu-Glu-Glu → many Glu-Glu ↑ H_2O	By hydrolysing many internal glycosidic bonds, maltose is ultimately produced. Amylases are found in saliva and in pancreatic juice
Pepsin	Protein	aa-aa-aa-aa → many aa-aa ↑ H_2O	By hydrolysing many internal peptide bonds, dipeptides are produced. Pepsin acts in the stomach
Lipase	Fat	CH_2OOCR CH_2OH | | $CHOOCR + H_2O → CHOH + 3RCOOH$ | | CH_2OOCR CH_2OH	By hydrolysing the ester bonds of triglycerides, glycerol and free fatty acids are produced. Lipase is found in the pancreatic juices
Lactase	Lactose	Lactose + H_2O → glucose + galactose	
Maltase	Maltose	Maltose + H_2O → glucose	
Sucrase (invertase)	Sucrose	Sucrose + H_2O → glucose + fructose	Small intestine: produced variously in pancreas and walls of the intestine
Chymotrypsin	Protein	Protein hydrolysis	
Trypsin	Protein	Protein hydrolysis	
Dipeptidases	Dipeptides	Dipeptides + H_2O → amino acids	

Table 5.5 Some reactions and enzymes of digestion. Note that all the reactions involve hydrolysis. The pH optima of each enzymes matches its environment, i.e. pH7 in the mouth; pH2 in the stomach and pH8–9 in the small intestine (duodenum). The set of different protein-hydrolysing enzymes are often called the *proteases* or the *proteolytic enzymes*.

■ ABSORPTION

Once formed, the small-moleculed soluble fuel must now face the barrier of the plasma membranes of the cells that line the tube of the small intestine. There is a large absorbing area as shown in Fig. 5.4. But how, precisely, do these molecules penetrate the plasma membrane and enter the cell? If you look back at Fig. 2.19 on page 23, you will see that protein molecules are embedded in the double layer that constitutes the cell membrane. In intestinal lining (epithelial) cells some of these protein molecules have roles as *trans-locase enzymes*, i.e. they catalyse the transport of specific molecules. This kind of enzyme-catalysed active transport involves the conversion of ATP to ADP, thus the absorption process is endergonic.

It is interesting to note that a variety of digestive defects can occur in humans. If, for example, the genes that code for the protein of the enzyme *lactase* are defective then lactase is not produced and a person with this inherited defect will show *milk intolerance* (i.e. lactose which is present in the milk will not be broken down.) This condition can be quite unpleasant and even serious. Because the lactose (milk sugar) is not digested it passes, unabsorbed, down into the gut where (a) it draws water, through its osmotic effect, out of the cells of the colon, and (b) it provides a rich fermentable nutrient for colonic bacteria. The results are watery faeces (i.e. diarrhoea) and the production and elimination of gaseous fermentation products produced by the colonic bacteria. Interestingly, milk intolerance, as a genetic trait, is more widely prevalent in Chinese people than those of other races. Another digestive defect is that of gall stones. These are accretions of solid cholesterol in bile which can reduce or stop the flow of fat-emulsifying bile into the intestine. This greatly reduces the digestion and absorption of fats and results in (a) fatty faeces (termed steatorrhoea) and (b) deficiencies of certain vitamins that are soluble in fat and should, therefore, have been absorbed along with the fat. The harmful effects of some of these conditions can be lessened by varying the diet.

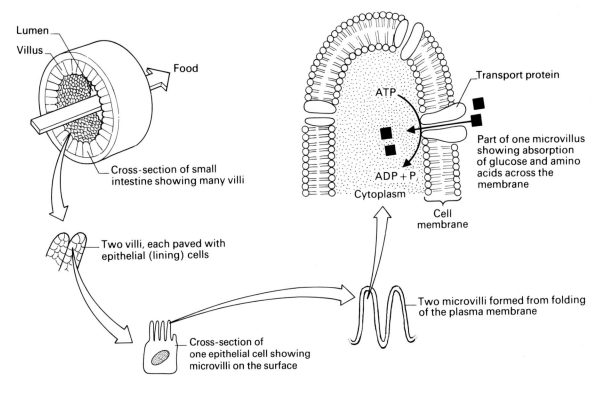

Figure 5.4 Intestinal absorption. As the semi-liquid mass of digested food moves along the tube of the small intestine the hydrolytic products of digestion are absorbed across the great surface area of membrane formed as a consequence of the arrangement of villi and microvilli. The transport proteins involved in active transport have channels through which absorbed molecules pass. ATP brings about changes in the *conformation* (shape) of these proteins, thus facilitating transport.

■ AFTER ABSORPTION – BUT BEFORE CATABOLISM

Now that absorption has been completed the immediate problem is to transport the absorbed molecules from the site of absorption to the tissues where they will ultimately be used, i.e. be catabolised. (This is the case whether we are talking about an earthworm, human or mushroom.)

In humans, the transport route involves the passage of blood from the intestinal capillaries to the liver via the *hepatic portal vein*. In the liver, when there is an adequate food supply, excess glucose is stored as glycogen. However, in times of comparative starvation, the glycogen is turned back into glucose. Amino acids are converted from one form to another in the liver and any excess amino acids are converted to glucose and glycogen. Some excess glucose, however, is also converted to a long-term storage compound, i.e. fat.

The liver, therefore, is like a 'station' on the transport route from the intestines to the fuel-hungry tissues. It functions as a sort of 'biochemical factory' for storing fuel molecules and converting them from one form into another.

The ultimate fate of the dissolved fuel molecules carried by the blood is to be oxidised in the tissues, yielding energy that is coupled to the production of ATP. The route includes passage through the heart and the lungs where oxygen is picked up (see Fig. 5.5). As we will see in Chapter 6, oxygen is the other vital reactant in the cellular biochemistry of respiration.

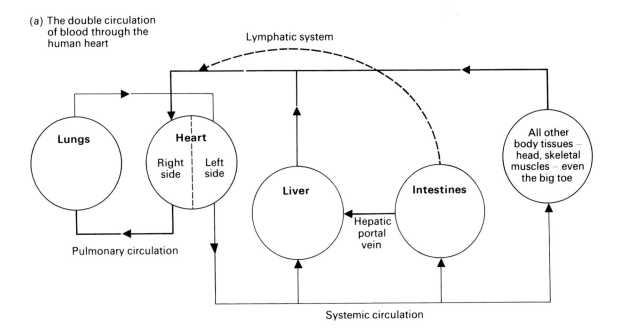

(a) The double circulation of blood through the human heart

Lymphatic system

Lungs

Heart

Right side | Left side

Liver

Intestines

All other body tissues – head, skeletal muscles – even the big toe

Hepatic portal vein

Pulmonary circulation

Systemic circulation

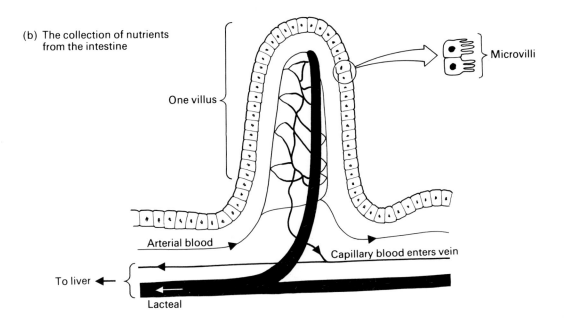

(b) The collection of nutrients from the intestine

Microvilli

One villus

Arterial blood

Capillary blood enters vein

To liver

Lacteal

Figure 5.5 The route from intestine to the big toe. Cells in all tissue beds *must* receive oxidisable fuels and oxygen. The scheme in (a) serves this purpose admirably. Glucose, amino acids and glycerol pass via the hepatic portal vein to the liver, where they are 'biochemically adjusted' (stored, interconverted, etc.). Fuels then pass to the heart. After oxygenation by the lungs, fuel-rich and oxygen-rich blood pass to the tissues via the systemic circulation. Note that absorbed fatty acids (and some incompletely digested monoglycerides are collected by the **lacteals**. These are branches of the lymphatic system and empty into venous blood at junctions near the armpits.

CHAPTER 6

THE METABOLISM OF HETEROTROPHS

■ INTRODUCTION

You will remember from the last chapter that we have a rich supply of nutrients dissolved in blood reaching all the tissues of our body. As well as dissolved glucose, there are amino acids, fat droplets, free fatty acids and some glycerol. Crucially, oxygen is there too, but mainly in chemical combination with the *haemoglobin* in the red cells. The dissolved nutrients and the oxygen pass out of the capillaries and into the fluid between the cells of the tissue. Then, with the help of the hormone insulin, glucose crosses the plasma membrane and enters the cell. The other nutrients also enter the cell as does the oxygen and now the 'biochemical carnival' can begin. The many different 'fuel' compounds are catabolised to carbon dioxide, water and, in the case of the amino acids, urea. ATP is made and new cell compounds are produced (see Fig. 6.1).

In this Chapter we will be discussing in more detail the ideas outlined in Fig. 6.1. First, we will deal with the oxidative catabolism of glucose. Then, we will consider what happens when the cells of a heterotroph become anaerobic and the organism is faced with the problem of obtaining some usable energy out of a fuel molecule *in the absence of oxygen*.

Finally, we will consider several other important aspects of the metabolism of heterotrophs. For example, there is the question of *other fuels*. How are all the other compounds that enter the cell catabolised? There is also the matter of biosynthesis, as Fig. 6.1 shows. Finally, there is the problem of *controlling* the whole system, i.e changing the rates of various metabolic processes and adjusting the balance between catabolism and anabolism.

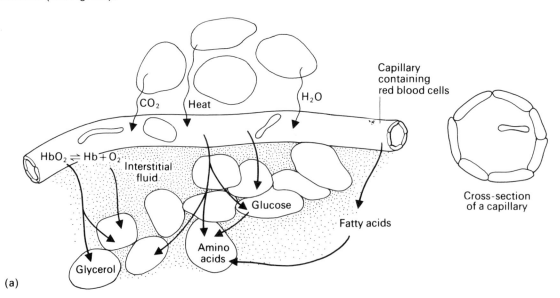

Figure 6.1 Animal metabolism in brief. Note that there are differences between tissues. Amino acids are broken down into CO_2, H_2O and urea in liver tissue.
(a) Capillaries deliver oxygen and nutrients to the cells in the tissue beds. The molecules move to the cell surfaces by diffusion down a concentration gradient. Metabolic heat, CO_2 and H_2O are removed by the capillaries. What happens *inside* cells is shown in part (b).

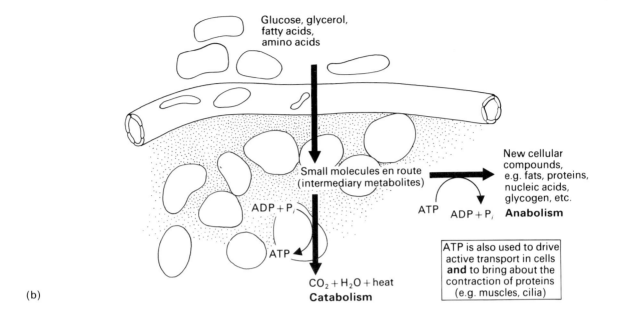

Glucose, glycerol, fatty acids, amino acids

Small molecules en route (intermediary metabolites)

New cellular compounds, e.g. fats, proteins, nucleic acids, glycogen, etc.

$ADP + P_i$

ATP $ADP + P_i$ **Anabolism**

ATP

$CO_2 + H_2O$ + heat

Catabolism

ATP is also used to drive active transport in cells **and** to bring about the contraction of proteins (e.g. muscles, cilia)

(b)

(b)   The principal biochemical processes that occur *inside* each cell. They are shown here 'on top' of cells to illustrate the relationship between cellular metabolism, interstitial fluid and capillaries.

■ OXIDATIVE CATABOLISM OF GLUCOSE: THE FOUR STAGES

Aided by insulin, the vital components glucose and oxygen have penetrated the cell and now confront the range of destructive enzymes that face them. After about forty or so reactions, grouped into four distinct stages, each glucose molecule will have been 'ripped to pieces' and eventually released (in exhaled breath!) as CO_2 and H_2O. The oxygen molecules that entered the cell with the glucose will have been the oxidising agent in this destruction of the glucose. So, let us examine what occurs in more detail.

When glucose is absorbed into the body, it undergoes exactly the same overall reaction as happens when you plunge a spoonful of smouldering glucose into a gas jar of oxygen. The overall reaction is as follows:

$$C_6H_{12}O_6 + 6O_2 \longrightarrow 6CO_2 + 6H_2O$$

(Energy out = $2900 \, kJ \, mol^{-1}$)

As you can see, oxygen is the oxidising agent in this reaction and is itself reduced to water. Much energy is released; in the gas jar version of the reac-

tion most of the 2900 kilojoules appear as heat. *In vivo*, a 'furnace' of this kind would be a biological hazard. Tissues are built of proteins and proteins denature at around 40°C, so no process of catabolism could possibly allow heat to be released faster than the cooling systems (i.e. of blood, sweat, etc.) could cope with. Ordinary 'burning', therefore, is not feasible.

Another reason that makes the idea of 'burning' entirely inappropriate is that catabolism *must* be controlled. The organism must be able to regulate the release of energy from its fuel (for example, reading these pages has a different energy requirement than running for a bus). To achieve such control, something much more subtle than just one giant reaction which releases nearly three thousand kilojoules per mole of glucose is required.

Just such a system has evolved over the course of billions of years. It involves four distinct but linked stages which occur in the following order:

1. glycolysis;
2. the link reaction;
3. Krebs cycle;
4. the electron transport chain.

Taken together these four stages constitute what is referred to as the complete *aerobic catabolism of glucose* (this is the correct name for the 'ripping to pieces' of glucose that we described in the beginning of this Section). The outcome of this scheme of aerobic catabolism is that the overall reaction

$$C_6H_{12}O_6 + 6O_2 \longrightarrow 6CO_2 + 6H_2O$$

is simply spread out over the forty or so reactions that make up the four stages. The energy, which is still 2900 kJ for each mole catabolised, is released in small stages. Around 50% of the energy is trapped by the net formation of 38 moles of ATP from 38ADP and 38P$_i$ and the remainder is released (in a controlled manner) as heat. The two modes of energy release, i.e. that seen *in vitro* in a gas jar and *in vivo* in an organism, are compared in Fig. 6.2.

Before outlining and then detailing the four stages of energy release, we will place them into the context of the cell structure. Figure 6.3 is a drawing based on an electron micrograph of a liver cell and shows exactly what happens and where. In fact, of the four stages only glycolysis occurs in the cytoplasm. The products of this initial, enzyme-catalysed process then pass right into the centre (i.e. *matrix*) of the nearest mitochondrion where the enzymes of the link reaction and the Krebs cycle are found. Finally, the rather insoluble components of the electron transport chain are found 'studded' into the inner membrane of each mitochondrion.

The aim of the four stages (one in the cytoplasm and three in the mitochondria) is to accomplish the overall reaction of glucose oxidation in such a way that about half the energy available is 'usefully trapped' as 38ATP and the other half is released gradually and harmlessly as heat. What happens at the various stages?

The glucose molecule can reasonably be regarded as a carbon atom framework with a cargo of hydrogen atoms attached. Throughout the first three stages, the hydrogens are progressively 'stripped off' the carbon atoms and carried away attached to hydrogen carrying coenzymes, mostly as NADH/H$^+$ although at one place in the Krebs cycle they are carried away as FADH$_2$. The carbon atoms of the glucose ring are converted to carbon dioxide, with the oxygen atoms of the carbon dioxide coming as a sort of 'loan' from water. If you remove oxygen from water you are left with two hydrogen atoms and

again these are carried away by NAD$^+$ in the form of NADH/H$^+$. By the time the glucose has been dismembered in this way (i.e. by glycolysis + link reaction + Krebs cycle), all six carbon dioxide (6CO$_2$) molecules of the overall equation have been produced, no oxygen has been used, and a large number of reduced coenzymes have been produced (in fact 10NADH/H$^+$ and 2FADH$_2$).

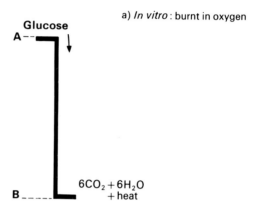

a) *In vitro*: burnt in oxygen

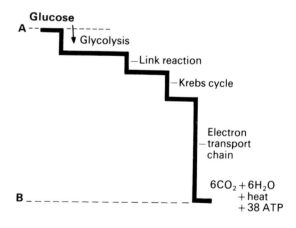

b) *In vivo*: catabolised in cells

Figure 6.2   The energy difference between A and B is 2900 kJ mol^{-1}. *In vitro* this is released in one step, entirely as heat. *In vivo* the four stages release the same amount of energy gradually. Most energy (hence most ATP) is made in the electron transport chain. However, as this stage occurs twelve times (see later) for each glucose dealt with, the energy is, once again, released gradually.

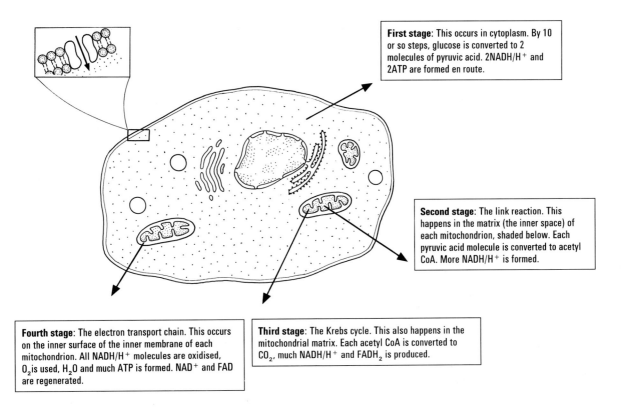

Entry: Glucose crosses the plasma membrane through the agency of transport proteins. Insulin is involved, as is ATP.

First stage: This occurs in cytoplasm. By 10 or so steps, glucose is converted to 2 molecules of pyruvic acid. 2NADH/H$^+$ and 2ATP are formed en route.

Second stage: The link reaction. This happens in the matrix (the inner space) of each mitochondrion, shaded below. Each pyruvic acid molecule is converted to acetyl CoA. More NADH/H$^+$ is formed.

Third stage: The Krebs cycle. This also happens in the mitochondrial matrix. Each acetyl CoA is converted to CO_2, much NADH/H$^+$ and FADH$_2$ is produced.

Fourth stage: The electron transport chain. This occurs on the inner surface of the inner membrane of each mitochondrion. All NADH/H$^+$ molecules are oxidised, O_2 is used, H_2O and much ATP is formed. NAD$^+$ and FAD are regenerated.

Figure 6.3 Glucose entry to the cell and the four stages of energy release from this glucose.

This then brings us to the fourth stage, the electron transport chain (ETC for short). In this stage, all the reduced coenzymes produced in the first three stages react with molecular oxygen to give water and regenerated NAD$^+$ and FAD. In fact, twelve molecules of water (12H$_2$O) are produced and these more than repay those that were used up during the first three stages. During the 'glucose dismemberment' process, energy is progressively released, some as heat and some in the form of the 38ATP mentioned earlier. Most of the ATP, i.e. 34 out of the 38ATP molecules, are produced in the electron transport chain.

The above two paragraphs compress into a few lines a long and very complicated process. Look now at Fig. 6.4(a) which summarises the sequence of stages in a fairly formal way, and Fig. 6.4(b) which, in a more informal style, emphasises the 'progressive dismemberment' idea of the four stages of aerobic catabolism of glucose. If you can follow and understand fully the stages as outlined in Fig. 6.4(a) you will achieve a large part of what is required.

■ **SOME FURTHER DETAIL**

You will need to understand at least some of the detail that follows to make the best of the discussions on anaerobic catabolism, other fuels, biosynthesis and control that follow later in this chapter. Let's look at each stage, separately.

(a)

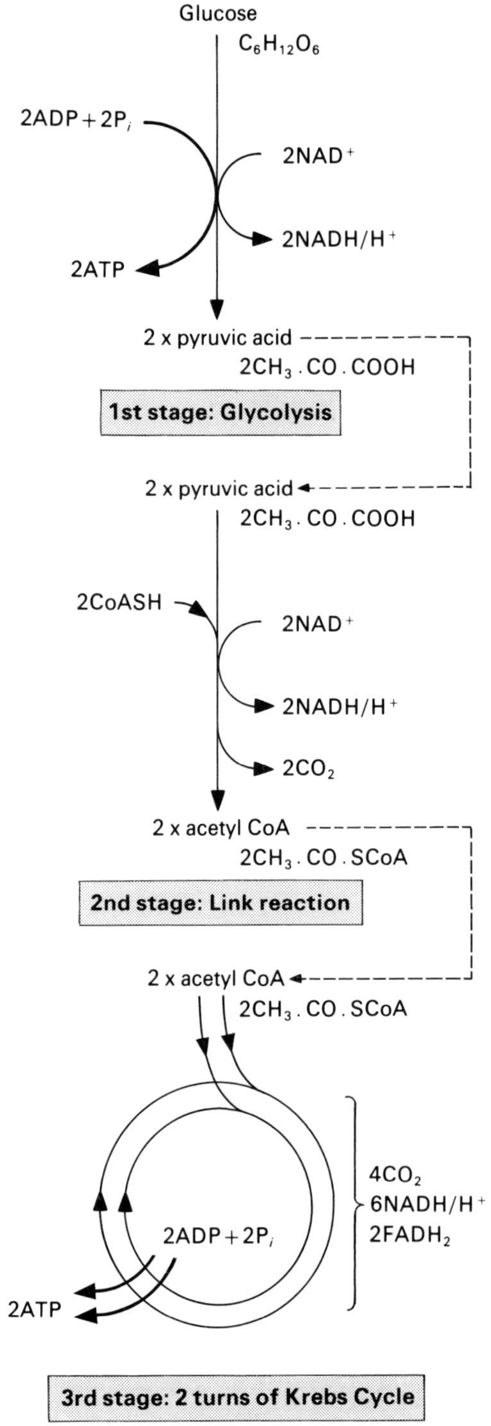

Glucose
$C_6H_{12}O_6$

$2ADP + 2P_i$

$2NAD^+$

$2NADH/H^+$

$2ATP$

2 x pyruvic acid
$2CH_3.CO.COOH$

1st stage: Glycolysis

2 x pyruvic acid
$2CH_3.CO.COOH$

$2CoASH$

$2NAD^+$

$2NADH/H^+$

$2CO_2$

2 x acetyl CoA
$2CH_3.CO.SCoA$

2nd stage: Link reaction

2 x acetyl CoA
$2CH_3.CO.SCoA$

$4CO_2$
$6NADH/H^+$
$2FADH_2$

$2ADP + 2P_i$

$2ATP$

3rd stage: 2 turns of Krebs Cycle

(a) Note: $6H_2O$ are 'lent' in these stages.

The 10NADH/H$^+$ and 2FADH$_2$ produced during the first three stages are then dealt with by the fourth stage as follows:

$$\left. \begin{array}{l} \text{10 NADH/H}^+ + 5O_2 \longrightarrow \text{10 NAD}^+ + \text{10 H}_2O \\ \text{2 FADH}_2 \quad + \quad O_2 \longrightarrow \text{2 FAD} \ + \ 2H_2O \end{array} \right\} + 34 \text{ ATP}$$

4th stage: Electron transport chain

(b)

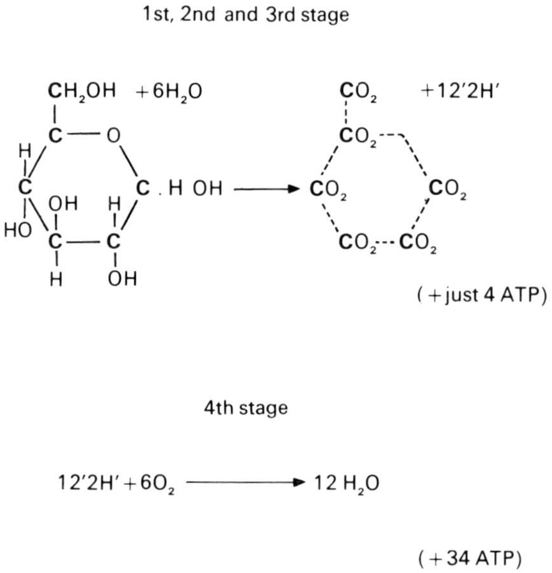

1st, 2nd and 3rd stage

$CH_2OH \quad +6H_2O$

$CO_2 \quad +12'2H'$

$(+$ just 4 ATP$)$

4th stage

$$12'2H' + 6O_2 \longrightarrow 12 H_2O$$

$(+34$ ATP$)$

(b) This representation shows how glucose is 'stripped' of hydrogens in the first three stages, the carbon atoms being converted to CO_2. In the fourth stage all the 'stripped out' hydrogens (carried as reduced coenzymes) are oxidised.

Figure 6.4 Some details of the four stages of glucose catabolism. Without reading any further you should be able to satisfy yourself that the sum of the four stages in (a) is $C_6H_{12}O_6 + 6O_2 \rightarrow 6CO_2 + 6H_2O$ and that 38ATPs are made. Check also that all the atoms balance in (b).

■ GLYCOLYSIS

$$C_6H_{12}O_6 + 2NAD^+ \longrightarrow 2C_3H_4O_3 + 2NADH/H^+$$

As you read the following you should refer where necessary to Fig. 6.5. The main features of the glycolysis pathway are shown in Fig. 6.5(a) and you may need to be able to reproduce this diagram for yourself. Figure 6.5(b) contains more detail if you require it out of interest.

The word glyco-lysis simply means 'sugar-splitting'. Pyruvic acid has the formula $CH_3.CO.COOH$. Adding up the number of each atom we get $C_3H_4O_3$. If the cell converts *one* molecule of glucose, i.e. $C_6H_{12}O_6$ into *two* molecules of $C_3H_4O_3$, then comparing the numbers of atoms in each, it isn't hard to see that the only change is the loss of four hydrogen atoms. These hydrogens make their appearance in two molecules of reduced NAD^+ (i.e. $NADH/H^+$). Count the H atoms on both sides of the formula shown (above right) and you will see that $12 = 8 + 4$.

In fact, this conversion of glucose takes place over ten steps involving a number of sugar phosphates: glucose becomes glucose-1-phosphate which becomes glucose-6-phosphate which becomes fructose-6-phosphate and so on (see Fig. 6.5 (b)). All of these compounds are the *substrates* (see Chapter 3, page 32) for the enzymes of glycolysis. During the sequence of reactions of glycolysis, some of the phosphate compounds have sufficient chemical energy to be able to pass their phosphate directly on to ADP and so make an ATP. In fact, in glycolysis two ATPs are made in this way. Any process that makes ATP *in vivo* is called phosphorylation. Because these ATP molecules are formed from the actual substrates of the metabolic pathway, the ATP-making process is called *substrate level phosphorylation*.

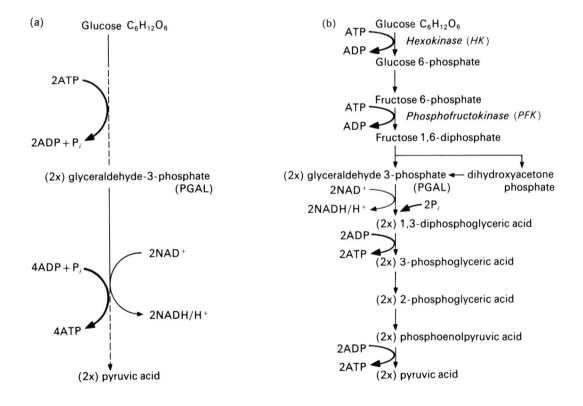

Figure 6.5 Glycolysis. Although you do not need to know the detail in part (b), look at it carefully. It is a good example of a metabolic pathway: each step is catalysed by a different enzyme, although only two are named here. The various substances are collectively termed 'intermediary metabolites'. You should be able to see that (a) is a condensed version of (b).

If you study Fig. 6.5(b) carefully, you should be able to note the following:

● glucose is converted to glucose-6-phosphate by the enzyme *hexokinase*. This requires magnesium ions as an activator (see Chapter 5);

● the conversion of fructose-6-phosphate to fructose-1,6-diphosphate is catalysed by the enzyme *phosphofructokinase* (PFK). This is a very important regulatory enzyme (see page 87);

● two C_3 (three-carbon) molecules are produced from one C_6 (six-carbon) molecule when fructose-1,6-diphosphate 'breaks in two';

● glucose has to be activated by reacting it with one ATP in the first step. Later fructose-6-phosphate reacts with a second ATP. This kind of 'energy pump-priming' is more than repaid when *four* ATP molecules are made by substrate level phosphorylation. Therefore, there is a net gain of *two* ATP molecules.

● $NADH/H^+$ is made when 3-phosphoglyceraldehyde (PGAL) is oxidised to 1,3-diphosphoglyceric acid (PGA). Because *two* molecules of PGAL are formed from *one* glucose, *two* molecules of $NADH/H^+$ are formed altogether.

■ THE LINK REACTION

After pyruvic acid is formed, it diffuses from cytoplasm to the mitochondria (see Box 6.1) and penetrates the inner mitochondrial membrane. Here, in the mitochondrial matrix it undergoes the link reaction. The link reaction is so named because it links the first and third stages of glucose catabolism. It converts the pyruvic acid formed by glycolysis to acetyl coenzyme A (acetyl CoA) which then enters the Krebs cycle. The overall reaction is catalysed by the enzyme pyuvate dehydrogenase complex (PDC) and can be shown as follows:

$$CoA + CH_3.CO.COOH \xrightarrow{PDC} CH_3.CO \sim CoA + CO_2$$

Pyruvic acid   Acetic acid

$$NAD^+ \qquad NADH/H^+$$

As you can see from the carbon atoms printed in bold type, the conversion is:

$$C_3 \rightarrow C_2 + C_1$$

Once again, *one* molecule of $NADH/H^+$ is formed from each of the *two* pyruvic acid molecules. The two carbon compound acetyl CoA is, in fact, an acetyl group activated by a special coenzyme called coenzyme A (CoA for short). You met this coenzyme on page 63 of Chapter 5. The enzyme PDC occurs in solution in the mitochondrial matrix fluid.

■ THE KREBS CYCLE

Imagine what it is like inside a mitochondrion. There is a fluid filled matrix which stretches out in all directions. Here and there shelf-like projections of folded inner membrane (the cristae) stretch out into the matrix. Dissolved in the matrix are many millions of acetyl CoA molecules that have been made by the link reaction. There are two carbon atoms in each acetyl CoA (i.e. in the acetyl groups) and eventually each of these carbon atoms is destined to form a carbon dioxide molecule. How will this happen?

One acetyl CoA molecule in the matrix begins its final act of fragmentaton by entering one of the millions of Krebs cycle sequences that are happening within this one mitochondrion. A four-carbon molecule approaches the acetyl CoA. The CoA part is 'pushed out', the C_4 joins to the acetyl (C_2) group and a C_6 molecule is formed. This then is converted to another compound then to another and another. As the cycle of conversions continues, each catalysed by its own enzyme, the molecule gets smaller and smaller and is converted eventually into a C_4 molecule as shown here:

$$C_6 \rightarrow C_6 \rightarrow C_6 \rightarrow C_5 \rightarrow C_4 \rightarrow C_4 \rightarrow C_4 \rightarrow C_4$$

The final C_4 molecule is the same compound that initially combined with an acetyl CoA (i.e. it has been regenerated, hence the term 'cycle'), and is now able to combine with more C_2 groups as the cyclic sequence of reactions continues.

Returning to a more orthodox method of description, look at Fig. 6.6. As well as the production of *two* CO_2 molecules as described (i.e. one CO_2 molecule

Mitochondria are present in all eukaryotic cells and convert the chemical potential energy of various metabolites into the chemical potential energy of ATP. This in turn drives all the energy-requiring processes in each cell. Some kinds of cell have very many mitochondria (often more than 1000 per cell), while other kinds of cell have just a few. The more energy a cell needs, the more mitochondria it has, e.g. liver cells, muscle fibres and sperm cells have many mitochondria.

Mitochondria possess DNA of their own (i.e. mitochondrial DNA) and it is generally believed that mitochondria have evolved from primitive bacteria-like organisms. Some 1.5 billion years ago, these bacteria-like organisms invaded primitive eukaryotic cells and, by living symbiotically inside them, 'became' the mitochondria of the cell. Modern mitochondria still synthesise many of their own proteins (they possess mRNA and tRNA molecules as well as DNA) and are able to change shape rapidly and move round the cell. Chapter 7 examines this *endosymbiont* theory in more detail. In fact, mitochondria are very similar in size to many modern bacteria, being (frequently but not always) a cylinder of 0.5–1 μm in diameter and around 10 μm in length. They contain two membranes, an outer very porous membrane and an inner selectively permeable and much folded membrane that surrounds a fluid-filled space called the *matrix*. The 'shelves' formed by the in-tucking (*invagination*) of the inner membrane are termed *cristae*.

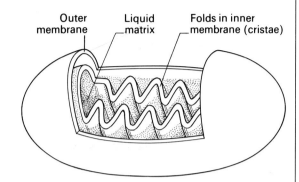

Outer membrane Liquid matrix Folds in inner membrane (cristae)

Figure 1

The outer membrane is permeable to all molecules with an RMM (relative molecular mass) of less than 10 000. It has a typical lipid bilayer studded with transport proteins. The inner membrane has an unusual structure and is less permeable: special transport mechanisms are involved in the movement of molecules or ions in and out of the matrix. All the components of the electron transport chain (see text) are embedded in the inner membrane, in addition to a number of molecules of an enzyme called *ATP synthetase*. In solution in the matrix are many copies of the enzymes involved in the link reaction and the Krebs cycle. Enzymes of fatty acid oxidation (discussed later in this chapter) are also dissolved in the liquid of the matrix.

from each acetyl CoA that enters the cycle), the many hydrogen atoms that are removed from the intermediates of the Krebs cycle are collected by hydrogen-carrying coenzymes: in fact for each turn of the cycle *three* molecules of NADH/H$^+$ and *one* of FADH$_2$ are produced. And once again, by substrate level phosphorylation, *one* ATP molecule is produced. As the cycle turns twice for each glucose molecule, the number of new molecules produced is multiplied by two. Therefore, in total, we have *six* NADH/H$^+$, *two* FADH$_2$ and *two* ATP molecules produced.

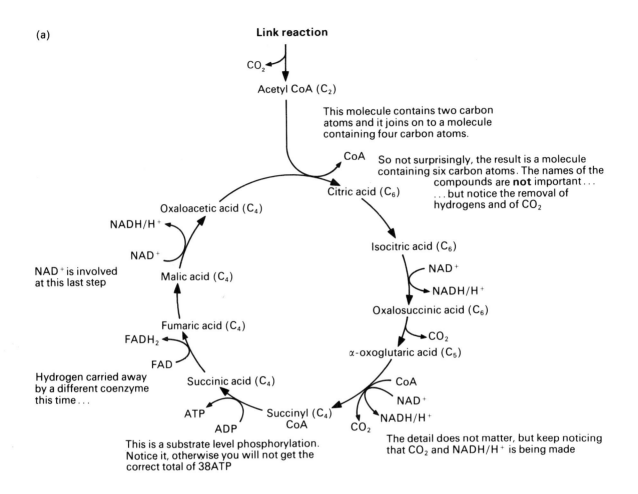

(a)

Link reaction

CO_2

Acetyl CoA (C_2)

This molecule contains two carbon atoms and it joins on to a molecule containing four carbon atoms.

CoA

So not surprisingly, the result is a molecule containing six carbon atoms. The names of the compounds are **not** important ... ... but notice the removal of hydrogens and of CO_2

Citric acid (C_6)

Oxaloacetic acid (C_4)

NADH/H$^+$

NAD$^+$

NAD$^+$ is involved at this last step

Malic acid (C_4)

Isocitric acid (C_6)

NAD$^+$

NADH/H$^+$

Oxalosuccinic acid (C_6)

CO_2

Fumaric acid (C_4)

FADH$_2$

FAD

α-oxoglutaric acid (C_5)

Hydrogen carried away by a different coenzyme this time ...

Succinic acid (C_4)

CoA

NAD$^+$

NADH/H$^+$

ATP

ADP

Succinyl (C_4) CoA

CO_2

This is a substrate level phosphorylation. Notice it, otherwise you will not get the correct total of 38ATP

The detail does not matter, but keep noticing that CO_2 and NADH/H$^+$ is being made

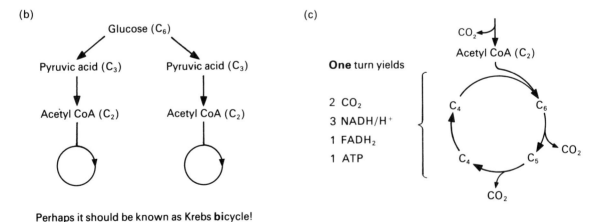

(b)

Glucose (C_6)

Pyruvic acid (C_3) Pyruvic acid (C_3)

Acetyl CoA (C_2) Acetyl CoA (C_2)

Perhaps it should be known as Krebs **bi**cycle!

(c)

CO_2

Acetyl CoA (C_2)

One turn yields

2 CO_2

3 NADH/H$^+$

1 FADH$_2$

1 ATP

C_4 C_6

CO_2

C_4 C_5

CO_2

Figure 6.6   The Krebs cycle. **Learn** parts (b) and (c) but **look at** (a) carefully – it will help you to understand the basics. You met the enzyme that catalyses the step succinic acid → fumaric acid in Chapter 3, it is called *succinic dehydrogenase*. Remember that the Krebs cycle turns **twice** for each glucose catalysed.

■ THE ELECTRON TRANSPORT CHAIN AND OXIDATIVE PHOSPHORYLATION

Consider the metabolic tally at this point. Just four ATP molecules have been produced: a net gain of two from substrate level phosphorylation in glycolysis, and two from the substrate level phosphorylation that accompanies two turns of the Krebs cycle. There are, however, the many molecules of reduced coenzyme (i.e. NADH/H$^+$ and FADH$_2$) to be oxidised.

 Look back at Fig. 6.4(a) and work out, for one molecule of glucose, how many molecules of NADH/H$^+$ and FADH$_2$ are made altogether. Where precisely are they made?

Two molecules of NADH/H$^+$ are made in glycolysis, two in the link reaction and three in each turn of the Krebs cycle, making ten altogether. In addition, two molecules of FADH$_2$ are made in the two turns of the Krebs cycle. Each reduced coenzyme, whether NADH/H$^+$ or FADH$_2$ is oxidised by the electron transport chain in a *stepwise* manner. The release of energy that occurs during this stepwise process leads to more ATP production. As molecular oxygen is involved, this kind of ATP-making is called *oxidative phosphorylation*.

Experiments show that a total of three ATP molecules are made for each molecule of NADH/H$^+$ oxidised and two ATP molecules for each molecule of FADH$_2$ oxidised. Since ten NADH/H$^+$ and two FADH$_2$ are made altogether, it is easy to calculate that the total number of $(10 \times 3) + (2 \times 2) = 34$ molecules of ATP are made by oxidative phosphorylation. Adding 34ATP to the 4ATP made by substrate level phosphorylation gives the total of 38ATP that we are expecting. Table 6.1 provides a reminder of the types and location of ATP production in glucose catabolism.

 What is meant by 'stepwise' oxidation of the reduced coenzymes?

The overall reactions are as follows:

Reaction 1
$$NADH/H^+ + \tfrac{1}{2}O_2 \longrightarrow NAD^+ + H_2O \text{ (3ATP made)}$$

Reaction 2
$$FADH_2 + \tfrac{1}{2}O_2 \longrightarrow FAD + H_2O \text{ (2ATP made)}$$

Both of these overall reactions, however, occur by means of a series of linked reduction/oxidation reactions in which the reduced coenzyme is the initial reducing agent and molecular oxygen is the final oxidising agent. Imagine these linked reactions as a kind of relay race in which a number of runners (carriers) pass batons (electrons or hydrogen atoms) down the line from the starting point (NADH/H$^+$ or FADH$_2$) to the finishing point (molecular oxygen). As the baton passes from one carrier to the next the energy available from the oxidation of *one* mole of NADH/H$^+$ is progressively released with the associated formation of *three* ATPs and heat. Similarly, *one* mole of FADH$_2$ generates *two* ATPs and heat. This process is oxidative phosphorylation. Look now at Fig. 6.7.

Stage	Location in the cell	Type of phosphorylation	Net number of ATPS produced per molecule of glucose
Glycolysis	Cytoplasm	Substrate level	2
Link reaction	Matrix of mitochondrion	None	0
Krebs cycle	Matrix of mitochondrion	Substrate level	2
Electron transport chain	Inner membrane of mitochondrion	Oxidative	34

Table 6.1 ATP production in cells. The total of 38 is the value most commonly quoted. In fact, 2ATP are (usually) used up in transporting some of the metabolites across the inner mitochondrial membrane – so the value of 36 is often seen in some texts. As long as you know why there are these two values, either is acceptable.

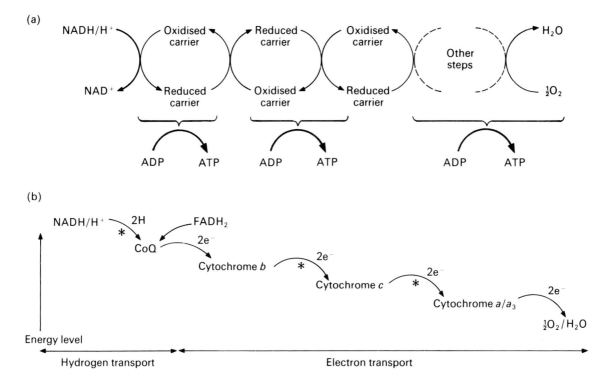

(a)

NADH/H$^+$ → Oxidised carrier → Reduced carrier → Oxidised carrier — Other steps → H$_2$O

NAD$^+$ → Reduced carrier → Oxidised carrier → Reduced carrier — $\frac{1}{2}$O$_2$

ADP   ATP   ADP   ATP   ADP   ATP

(b)

NADH/H$^+$ ⟍ 2H
   *
    ↘ CoQ ⟍ FADH$_2$
         2e$^-$
         Cytochrome b ⟍ 2e$^-$
               *
               Cytochrome c ⟍ 2e$^-$
                     *
                     Cytochrome a/a_3 ⟍ 2e$^-$
                           $\frac{1}{2}$O$_2$/H$_2$O

Energy level

Hydrogen transport   Electron transport

Figure 6.7 The electron transport chain. Either of these two simplified diagrams is a reasonable representation. (a) shows the idea of alternate redox reactions with molecular oxygen as the final oxidising agent (i.e. final electron acceptor). (b) shows how NADH/H$^+$ and FADH$_2$ join the same route. Each ATP-making step is shown as an asterisk.

As you can see, the electron transport chain (ETC) is an assembly of proteins and other substances that transports two hydrogen atoms or electrons from each molecule of either NADH/H$^+$ or FADH$_2$ to molecular oxygen. The components that make up the chain include among others a carrier known as *coenzyme Q* and a number of different iron-containing proteins collectively called the *cytochromes*. As electrons pass down the chain, the carriers undergo the redox reactions mentioned above. At specific points in the sequence, the synthesis of ATP molecules occurs: three ATPs per pair of electrons (i.e. pair of hydrogens) if NADH/H$^+$ is the source, and two ATPs per pair of electrons (i.e. pair of hydrogens) if FADH$_2$ is the source. This oxidative phosphorylation is, therefore, tightly *coupled* to electron transport. Box 6.2 gives more detail of the supposed *mechanism* of ATP production and also coupling.

There are at least four different cytochromes involved (left to right) in the electron transport chain (see Fig. 6.7(b)). These are cytochrome b, cyto-

chrome c, cytochrome a and cytochrome a_3. All of these are proteins that contain a haem prosthetic group. This is the same group as is involved in haemoglobin, although in the case of the cytochromes (unlike haemoglobin) the iron atom is alternately reduced to iron(II) and oxidised to iron(III), i.e. Fe^{2+} ↔ Fe^{3+}.

The last cytochrome, cytochrome a_3, has two points of particular interest: (a) as well as containing iron, it also contains copper (a crucially important use of this trace element) and (b) cytochrome a_3 is the component to which a cyanide ion irreversibly binds if present in the organism. This very toxic ion is well known in 'whodunit' novels, more seriously known in industrial pollution and more grimly known as an agent of judicial execution. Cyanide creates its life-destroying effect by so completely binding with cytochrome a_3 that oxygen is excluded from the ETC. Thus, all oxidative phosphorylation ceases, all oxygen consumption is prevented, and death ensues.

■ BOX 6.2   MECHANISM OF OXIDATIVE PHOSPHORYLATION

By the mid 1950s biochemists were clear enough about the essential role of ATP as the major *energy transducer* in cells; its role in 'leading energy across' from food molecules to biosynthesis, muscular work and active transport. The key part played by mito-chondria was clear: $NADH/H^+$ and $FADH_2$ were indeed oxidised within these cells. They made almost all of the cellular ATP. The sequence of electron transport chain components had been revealed by certain experiments. Other experiments had measured how many ATP molecules were made when one molecule of reduced coenzyme was oxidised by $\frac{1}{2}O_2$. Using 'P' to represent one ATP made and 'O' to represent one oxygen atom used, biochemists discovered that the P:O ratio was 3 for $NADH/H^+$ and the P:O ratio was 2 for $FADH_2$.

What no one knew, and what everyone argued about, was *how* the synthesis of ATP was *coupled* to the transport of electrons. Some people favoured the idea of the involvement of many phosphate inter-mediates (just as glycolysis, see Fig. 6.5(b)). Others favoured an ingenious alternative called the *chemiosmotic theory* of oxidative phosphorylation. This theory, proposed in 1961 by an English bio-chemist named Peter Mitchell, proved to be right (see Figure 1). It could even lead to an ideal slim-ming technique (see later on).

Many of the events in Figure 1(a) are by now a familiar story. Each $NADH/H^+$ (and $FADH_2$) pro-duced by stages 1, 2 and 3 is oxidised progressively by the ETC components. Note that the assembly of

black blobs represents one ETC chain: there is a large number of identical sets all over the entire inner membrane. However, energy from this electron transport forces hydrogen ions to move against a concentration gradient from the inside of the matrix to the space between the two membranes. Even-tually in Figure 1(b) the H^+ ions are allowed to flow back into the matrix through a special gate in the *ATP synthetase* molecule. As ions are flowing *with* the concentration gradient, energy is released and ATP is made: this is like active transport in reverse.

The making of ATP by ATP synthetase and the transport of electrons are very tightly coupled with probably an efficiency of well over 50%. If it were possible to *uncouple* the two processes (e.g. by making the inner membrane 'leaky'), a H^+ gradient could not build up. As a consequence, ATP would not be made and all the energy of respiration would appear as heat! This probably happens to some extent when certain animals come out of hibernation; it also occurs in some newly born animals when they must generate a lot of heat to survive. It can also happen when certain artificial chemicals are taken into cells, e.g. when an explosive (dinitrophenol) used in the First World War contaminated the skin of munition workers, their mitochondria were un-coupled, they became hot and thin and there were several deaths. A *safe* uncoupler could therefore lead to an ideal slimming technique (merely through heat loss).

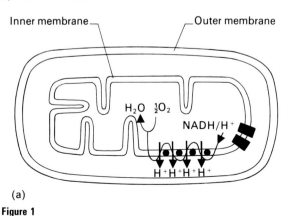

(a)

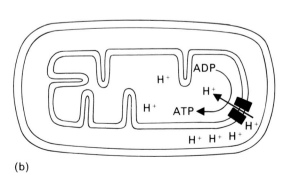

(b)

Figure 1

■ ANAEROBIC CATABOLISM: LIFE WITHOUT OXYGEN

Just what does an organism do when it does not have sufficient oxygen to 'drive' the electron transport chain? This happens all the time in a suspension of yeast cells in a vessel from which oxygen has been excluded. It also happens in our own muscles when a person runs at a speed which demands greater ATP production than the normal processes can provide and, as a result, the muscle tissue becomes *anaerobic*.

The cells, whether they are the unicells of yeast or the mass of cells in your calf muscle, get round the problem of an anaerobic intracellular environment by closing down the link reaction and the Krebs cycle and, of course, the ETC. Look back at Fig. 6.4(a). For each molecule of glucose that is converted to two molecules of pyruvic acid, two NADH/H$^+$ are formed. These reduced coenzymes cannot be dealt with by the ETC because there is no oxygen to act as the final electron acceptor. Nevertheless, unless all life is to grind to a halt, they have to be dealt with somehow. There are only microgram quantities of the hydrogen-carrying coenzymes and, to keep glycolysis going, the molecules of NADH/H$^+$ must somehow be reconverted to NAD$^+$.

The way cells carry out this reconversion when they run short of oxygen is to use *some other substance* produced inside the cell as an alternative oxidising agent. In our calf muscle cells that alternative oxidising agent is pyruvic acid itself. Figure 6.8 shows how this alternative system works.

Imagine that you are sprinting for a bus. Already you are breathing as fast and as hard as you can. Yet the ATP demands of your muscles are such that the rate of catabolism has far outstripped the supply of oxygen. The muscle fibres become more and more anaerobic. Catabolism does not, however, halt. The number of molecules of pyruvic acid produced by glycolysis exactly equals the number of molecules of NADH$^+$/H$^+$ produced. So, through the catalytic power of the enzyme *lactic dehydrogenase* (LDH), pyruvic acid is reduced by the NADH/H$^+$ to lactic acid. Thus reconverting the NADH/H$^+$ to NAD. The equation is simple and is worth looking at as it is easy to see exactly how the hydrogen atoms (shown in bold type) are 'collected' by the pyruvic acid.

$$CH_3 . CO . COOH + NAD\textbf{H}/\textbf{H}^+$$
$$\longrightarrow CH_3 . C\textbf{H}(O\textbf{H}) . COOH + NAD^+$$

The significance of this biochemical reaction is that it permits the production of at least some ATP in circumstances of limited or no oxygen. The yield is very low as all of the energy from ETC oxidative phosphorylation production and the substrate level phosphorylations of the Krebs cycle are unavailable. Nevertheless, two ATPs can be produced per molecule of glucose instead of none. Your muscles still can contract and enable you to catch that bus. However, under more demanding circumstances this anaerobic catabolism could be life saving, providing enough ATP to keep the heart and brain functioning until more oxygen is available.

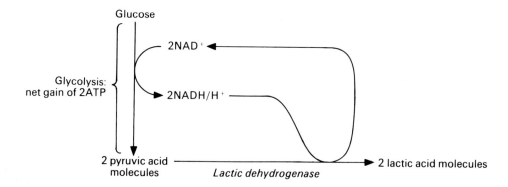

Figure 6.8 Anaerobic respiration in muscle. Exactly the same biochemistry is involved in lactic fermentations by certain bacteria. This is important commercially. The overall reaction is glucose → 2 lactic acid ($C_6H_{12}O_6 \rightarrow 2C_3H_6O_3$). Note that the terms 'anaerobic respiration' and 'anaerobic catabolism' are used interchangeably.

The process of anaerobic catabolism cannot continue for very long. The lactic acid that accumulates inside the cells progressively lowers the pH and this interferes with the functioning of the enzymes: you as the runner feel this effect as a cramp. When the sprint is over, the lactic acid that has piled up has to be re-oxidised to pyruvic acid which is then available for normal aerobic catabolism. This is done using the reverse of the reaction above, catalysed as before by LDH. The oxygen needed for this re-oxidation process (i.e. dealing with the excess $NADH/H^+$) causes you to continue to pant after resting. You are then said to be dealing with the *oxygen debt* that arose during anaerobic catabolism.

Some organisms can live indefinitely without oxygen. Indeed some bacteria cannot live in the presence of oxygen: these are termed *obligate anaerobes*. The bacteria that cause botulism and tetanus, *Clostridium botulinum* and *Clostridium tetani*, are examples of obligate anaerobes. Some organisms can live either aerobically or anaerobically according to the environment in which they find themselves. Yeast, for example, can oxidise glucose to carbon dioxide and water perfectly well. However, when the environment is anaerobic the ETC, Krebs cycle and link reaction are 'shut down'. As in muscle, the only ATP that is produced in the yeast is by the substrate level phosphorylation of glycolysis. Thus, once again only 2ATP instead of 38ATP are made per glucose. The NADH produced in that glycolysis is 'dumped'

not on pyruvic acid itself, but on a compound that is produced from pyruvic acid. The final outcome, as Fig. 6.9 shows, is the production of ethanol. This is formed by the reduction of *ethanal* which is itself formed from pyruvic acid by the removal of a carbon dioxide molecule.

Anaerobic catabolism in yeast is often called *fermentation*: thus one talks of 'yeast fermentation', or 'the fermentation of glucose by yeast' or 'alcoholic fermentation'. All the phrases mean the same thing and can be expressed as follows:

$$C_6H_{12}O_6 \longrightarrow 2C_2H_5OH + 2CO_2$$

The word fermentation is also used rather generally to mean any kind of anaerobic catabolism by bacteria or fungi. There are many kinds of substances other than glucose which can be used as a substrate for a whole range of organisms and many kinds of different products are formed. A number of fermentations are commercially or industrially important. The production of alcoholic drinks tends to be the obvious example when talking about yeast; however, the production of ethanol as a fuel is likely to become extremely important over the coming decades. As social and political pressure against burning fossil fuels increases, the 'gasohol' industry (in which purpose-grown plant material, usually sugar cane, is fermented to ethanol to provide vehicle fuel) is likely to grow substantially.

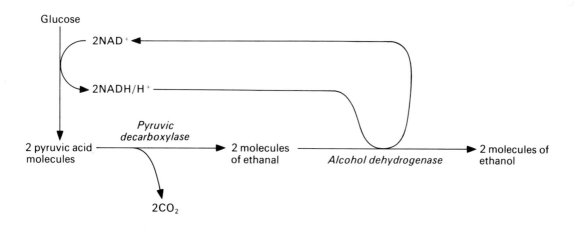

Figure 6.9 Anaerobic respiration in yeast. Both CO_2 and ethanol are made commercially by this fermentation. The overall reaction is glucose → 2 carbon dioxide + 2 ethanol ($C_6H_{12}O_6 \rightarrow 2CO_2 + 2C_2H_5OH$).

■ THE CATABOLISM OF OTHER COMPOUNDS

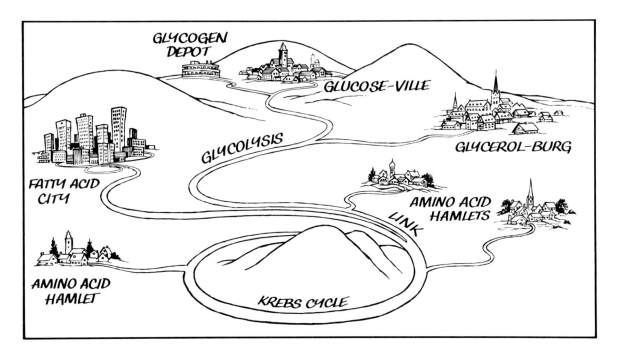

We now return our attention to aerobic catabolism, but this time we will look at nutrients other than glucose. As mentioned in the opening lines of this chapter, cells receive from the blood a mixture of fats, fatty acids, glycerol and amino acids. The question is therefore 'How do cells break down these compounds and make use of the chemical potential energy within them to make ATP?' This is no idle question of mere biochemical curiosity. You will have seen in Chapter 5 how human diet can contain great quantities of protein or of fat. And, in other animals, total carnivores for example, protein catabolism is clearly of central importance. And, not forgetting the smallest heterotrophs, what about bacteria and moulds growing on a lump of fat?

The good news from the point of view of the learner is that the catabolism of all compounds feeds into a number of *central metabolic pathways*. These central pathways are, essentially, the route by which glucose is catabolised. In other words, now that you have studied glucose catabolism, you will be able to apply the same principles to the other components.

Using a road system as a model for metabolic routes, you can imagine catabolism as 'all roads leading to the glucose road' as the cartoon above shows.

It is not quite as simple as this of course: it never is! Each of the other nutrients is broken down by its own supplementary path until it becomes an intermediate of glycolysis, the link reaction or the Krebs cycle. When this occurs, it joins the 'glucose road' and complete catabolism follows.

Amino acids
Alanine is one of the amino acids produced when proteins are digested. How is it catabolised? Look at the outline reaction shown below. The reaction is catalysed by a *transaminase* enzyme, in which the amino group of alanine is transferred from alanine to another acceptor compound. The compound on the left is alanine.

$$CH_3.CH(NH_2).COOH \rightarrow CH_3.CO.COOH + ''{-}NH_2''$$

(collected by an acceptor compound)

 Do you recognise the compound on the right formed from alanine?

You should have recognised the compound $CH_3.CO.COOH$ as pyruvic acid and this, of course, is the end-product of glycolysis. Pyruvic acid formed from alanine joins into the link reaction in the normal way. Figure 6.10 shows you how you can represent this kind of 'joining in' process using a very simple 'apple and stalk' diagram.

Other amino acids join into the central scheme (i.e. the 'apple and stalk' of Fig. 6.10) in the same way. A related point, of crucial biological importance, is what happens to the amino groups ($-NH_2$) that are removed from these amino acids. Box 6.3 gives details of this process.

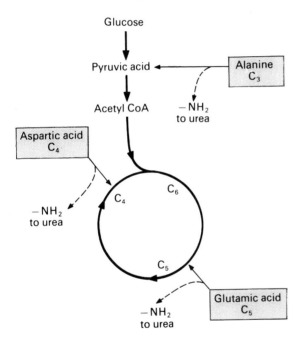

Figure 6.10 The central pathways. Alanine is catabolised to pyruvic acid which, in turn, is catabolised via the central pathways to CO_2 and H_2O. The amino acids glutamic acid and aspartic acid are converted to intermediates of the Krebs cycle. One way or another, **all** other amino acids join the 'apple and stalk' of the central pathways.

■ BOX 6.3 AMINO ACID CATABOLISM AND THE UREA CYCLE

As you will have seen in Chapter 5 (Fig. 5.3), proteins are in dynamic equilibrium with amino acids in the cells of all tissues. It is in the liver, however, that excess amino acids (carried there by the blood) are finally catabolised in mammals.

The catabolism of all 20 amino acids begins in the same way. First, the amino group is removed and the compound that remains is catabolised initially by its own specialised route and finally by joining in to the central pathways. Look back at the cartoon on page 82.

But what happens to the amino group that has been removed? In the liver of mammals, this amino group is converted to ammonia which, being very toxic, is rapidly converted to a soluble, unreactive, non-toxic compound called urea. The urea passes in the blood stream to the kidneys, at which point it is extracted from the blood (through glomerular filtration) and is concentrated in the urine.

The biochemistry of urea production in the liver was largely worked out in 1932 by Krebs and his co-worker Kurt Hensleheit. The overall reaction brought about by the urea cycle is as follows:

$$2NH_3 + CO_2 \rightarrow CO(NH_2)_2 + H_2O$$

Biochemistry, physiology and evolution all interrelate in the process of nitrogen excretion across the range of living organisms. Fish (and tadpoles) live in such a superabundance of water that the toxicity of ammonia doesn't matter, even at the sensitive embryonic stage. Therefore, these aquatic organisms 'don't bother with' with the urea cycle, they merely excrete the pure ammonia. At the embryonic stage of birds and reptiles, the organism lives in an environment that is very short of water, i.e. the egg. For this organism there is insufficient water to dissolve the urea. For this reason, the organism resorts to excreting insoluble nitrogenous compound, i.e. the white crystals of uric acid (familiar as bird lime). In birds and reptiles, therefore, evolution has produced other enzymes in place of the enzymes of the urea cycle to deal with the products of amino acid catabolism.

■ LIPIDS

We will now turn our attention to lipids, considering them as their component parts, glycerol and fatty acids. The metabolic fate of glycerol is fairly simple to describe in outline terms. In just two steps, glycerol is converted to an intermediate *dihydroxyacetone phosphate*. Unless you have an excellent memory for the detail in Fig. 6.5(b), you probably will not recognise this compound. It is, however, one of the two compounds formed in glycolysis when fructose-1,6-diphosphate breaks into two. Dihydroxyacetone phosphate is instantly converted into PGAL and joins the glucose pathway.

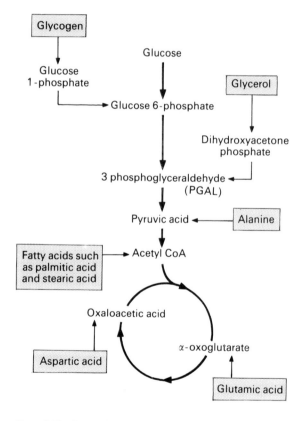

Figure 6.11 The catabolism of other compounds. Note how all the compounds in the shaded boxes have their own metabolic routes into the central pathways.

Q Attempt to draw your own 'apple and stalk' diagram for glycerol. Check it against the summary diagram in Fig. 6.11.

The supplementary pathway for fatty acids is longer and more complex than the previous nutrients we have discussed. It has, in fact, its own name, i.e. the *β-oxidation pathway*. The detail of this is not important at this level. The key point to note is that the common saturated fatty acids in fat, i.e. palmitic acid and stearic acid, both have an *even* number of carbon atoms in their molecules. Palmitic acid is $C_{15}H_{31}$.COOH and stearic acid is $C_{17}H_{35}$.COOH. The significance of this is that they are broken down by the β-oxidation pathway to a set of two-carbon (C_2) molecules that are then catabolised further.

Q What C_2 compound do you know of in any of the stages of glycolysis, the link reaction or the Krebs cycle? If palmitic acid is converted into this compound, how many molecules of it will be formed? What will then happen to those molecules?

The answer can only be one compound, the only C_2 compound in the entire set of central pathways, i.e. acetyl CoA. Given that palmitic acid has sixteen carbon atoms, eight acetyl CoA molecules are produced from palmitic acid by the β-oxidation pathway. These then enter the Krebs cycle in the normal way (see Fig. 6.11). Why is it called β-oxidation? A glance at the formula of palmitic acid below shows why.

To make acetyl groups from each 'CH_2CH_2' part of the chain involves oxidation. In fact this occurs in the usual way with water 'lending' the oxygen, and all the surplus hydrogen atoms being 'pulled out' as large quantities of $NADH/H^+$ which are then dealt with in the electron transport chain. Not surprisingly, with so many molecules of reduced coenzyme and acetyl CoA, large amounts of ATP are generated per molecule of fatty acid. This makes fat a much richer source of energy, both molecule for molecule and gram for gram than any of the other food types. Therefore, weight-watchers beware!

Palmitic acid CH_3CH_2.CH_2CH_2.CH_2CH_2.CH_2CH_2.CH_2CH_2.CH_2CH_2.CH_2CH_2.CH_2COOH

↓

8 acetyl CoAs

Before we finish this section, a word about glycogen is necessary. Unlike the other nutrients discussed above, glycogen is not brought to cells in the blood. It is largely insoluble and is an important food storage compound *within* cells. Thus, it is an intracellular nutrient and it is appropriate to consider here how the 'glucose residues' inside the glycogen molecule are catabolised. You might think that it is simply hydrolysed to glucose, but you would be wrong! It is split by an enzyme that makes use of a phosphate ion instead of water to form glucose-1-phosphate. This is then immediately converted by another enzyme into glucose-6-phosphate which you should recognise as the first intermediate of glycolysis. (Incidentally, glucose-6-phosphate can have its phosphate removed by a phosphatase enzyme to give free glucose. This is how glycogen helps maintain our blood sugar level.) Box 6.4 describes in more detail the role of glycogen in cells.

■ BOX 6.4   THE ROLE OF GLYCOGEN

You know from Chapter 2 that glycogen molecules are large branched-chain polymers of glucose. As they are relatively insoluble, glycogen granules make excellent cellular stores of 'reserve glucose'. Glucose is converted to glycogen after meals and reconverted to glucose in fasting periods between meals. In this way, regulation (i.e. homeostasis) of blood glucose is achieved between normal levels of 80 to 120 mg per 100 cm³ blood. This is physiologically important as the brain has no significant food stores and, if blood glucose falls much below the normal fasting level, unconsciousness may result.

The principal site of storage and glucose/glycogen interconversion is the liver. The hormones *insulin* and *glucagon* (produced by the pancreas) are much involved in the regulatory process. The details of hormone production and the way they act on glycogen biosynthesis and breakdown is another excellent example of the interdependence of biochemistry and physiology. Though the details are beyond the scope of this text, note that insulin stimulates glycogen *synthesis* and glucagon stimulates glycogen *break-down.*

When glycogen is mobilised, it is first converted to glucose-1-phosphate, which then becomes glucose-6-phosphate. Look back at Fig. 6.5(b) and see that glucose-6-phosphate is a glycolytic pathway intermediate. Thus, liver *can directly catabolise* glycogen right through to carbon dioxide and water. To replenish blood glucose, another enzyme is able to 'chop off' (i.e. hydrolyse) the phosphate of glucose-6-phosphate. The enzyme involved, *glucose-6-phosphatase*, is therefore very important in blood glucose regulation.

Muscle cells contain substantial amounts of stored glycogen. This makes biological sense as muscles need plenty of readily available fuel. In fact, muscles can only catabolise glycogen to carbon dioxide and water (or lactic acid, if conditions have become anaerobic). They do not have a phosphatase enzyme and so do not contribute to blood glucose regulation. The overall reactions can be summarised as shown below.

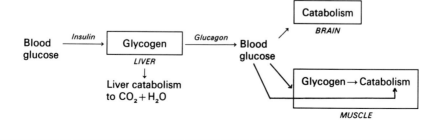

Figure 1

■ BIOSYNTHESIS IN HETEROTROPHS

If you consider the growth of an organism, you will realise that it is not just *energy* (in the form of ATP) that is required to make a fertilised fish egg into an adult salmon, or a baby into a twenty-stone wrestler; there is also a requirement for *materials*. You will know, already, that initially the materials are provided in the diet and then digested and transported to the cells of the organism. But how are the cell chemicals themselves actually made, i.e. biosynthesised?

The answer is that within each cell there are a large number of *biosynthetic pathways* (or anabolic pathways) by which the necessary intermediary metabolites are 'stitched together' to make the desired compounds.

How are these chemicals made from the intermediary metabolites? The detailed answer to this question is beyond the scope of this book. But you will know some simple answers. The process of protein synthesis was discussed in Chapter 4. You will also be familiar with the intermediary metabolites, i.e. the building blocks of biosynthesis.

Figure 6.12 outlines a few of these biosynthetic routes. Though the details are not important here, the *idea* that biosynthesis grows out of a pool of small molecules (intermediate metabolites) in the central pathways is most important. Indeed, in terms of the growth of an organism to the point at which it is large enough to be able to reproduce, biosynthesis is the mechanism behind this growth.

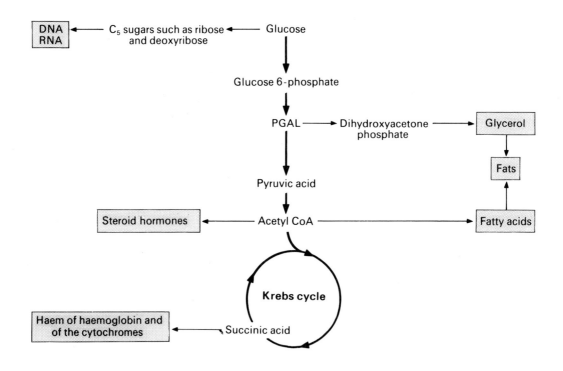

Figure 6.12 Some examples of biosynthesis showing how the precursors are intermediates in the central pathways. Most of these anabolic routes involve many steps. Conversion of ATP to ADP always occurs at some point or points in any biosynthetic pathway. Biosynthetic routes are almost always different in detail from catabolic routes; e.g. fatty acids are broken down *to* acetyl CoA by a different sequence of enzyme-catalysed reactions to those involved in making fatty acids *from* acetyl CoA. These differences have evolved to assist *metabolic control*. To have just one pathway for both biosynthesis and breakdown would be like trying to make one escalator serve ascending and descending passengers on the London Underground!

■ CONTROL OF METABOLISM

When a glucose molecule enters a cell there are several different things that can happen to it, or in biochemical terms, there are several possible *metabolic fates*. You will have come across some of these already. The glucose can be catabolised to carbon dioxide and water or it can be converted to stored glycogen. Indeed, it can also be converted to acetyl CoA and then into long-chain fatty acids and fat. It can in fact be dealt with by yet another pathway altogether that enables 5-carbon sugars, i.e. ribose and deoxyribose, to be formed from it. This diversity of possible metabolic fates is summed up in Fig. 6.13.

How does the cell 'know' whether to 'burn up' the glucose, 'lay it down' as glycogen or fat food store, or 'change' it into ribose in order to make RNA? What

controls the metabolism, determining which of the various processes occurs?

And, of course, it is not just a question of *which* pathway, it is also a question of *rate* (for example, the wrestler mentioned in the last section needs to catabolise glucose much faster in the middle of Round One than when he is sleeping some hours later).

It is mainly (though not quite exclusively) through enzymes that metabolism is regulated. Look carefully at Fig. 6.13. If the enzymes in pathway A are the most active, then glucose will be catabolised mainly along pathway A. If the enzymes in pathway B become more active, then glucose will follow this pathway.

Sometimes, the crudest form of 'enzyme activity control' is employed by cells, i.e. a cell may produce lots of enzyme X or none of enzyme X. If there is 'no enzyme' this means that there is 'no reaction' and hence 'no activity along that route'. The terms used to describe the production or non-production of an enzyme as a method of metabolic control are *enzyme induction* and *enzyme repression*. You do not need to know much about this except that the phenomenon of control exists. It tends to be a long term method of control; for example, if you drink alcohol regularly your liver tends to produce much more of the enzyme *alcohol dehydrogenase* which will catabolise the reaction to detoxify the alcohol.

A more common form of enzyme activity control is the phenomenon of *allostery*. You will have been introduced to this briefly in Chapter 3. In a given pathway, the reactions catalysed by certain enzymes, i.e. the ones that work the slowest in a sequence of reactions, are the *rate-limiting* steps of that pathway. If you control the rate of reaction at a point along the pathway you will control the rate of the whole pathway.

Consider the step in glycolysis which is catalysed by the enzyme *phosphofructokinase* (PFK). Look back at Fig. 6.5(b). The conversion of fructose-6-phosphate to fructose-1,6-diphosphate is the rate limiting step and so the activity of PFK will control the whole pathway. (The mechanism of this control will be explained later.) The activity of PFK is *greater in the presence of ADP or NAD$^+$*, and in contrast the activity of PFK is *less in the presence of ATP or NADH*.

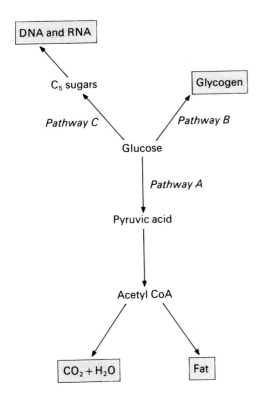

Figure 6.13 When glucose is eaten, its carbon atoms may find their way to CO_2, or fat, or glycogen or DNA and RNA. Initially there are three possible alternatives. What regulates the choice between pathways A, B and C?

Q Does this last sentence make regulatory SENSE? Think about this question before reading on.

When glycolysis, the link reaction, the Krebs cycle and the ETC have been 'overactive', will there be an excess of ATP and NADH/H$^+$ or will there be an excess of ADP and NAD$^+$? Which of these substances could, sensibly, act on PFK (a reaction that occurs early in the sequence) to slow the whole pathway down and so help the excess to be used up? You should be able to work out that if catabolism has been working at a rate greater than necessary in terms of the body's needs, there will be an excess of ATP and NADH/H$^+$. Thus, the fact that these substances act on PFK to reduce its activity is exactly what we would expect. Conversely, the (experimental) fact that ADP and NAD$^+$ increase the activity of PFK is, once again, what we would expect.

This kind of control is called *negative feedback* and is similar in 'control principle' to the way in which a central heating system is controlled, i.e. if the temperature gets too hot, the thermostat feeds back a signal that switches off the boiler; if it gets too cold, the converse happens.

How is the protein structure of the enzyme PFK able to respond to the presence or absence of the inhibitory substances (i.e. ATP and NADH/H$^+$) and activating substances (i.e. ADP and NAD$^+$)? The answer is that they bind to the enzyme at some *other site* to the site that the substrate (i.e. fructose-6-phosphate) binds to, and in so doing alter the active site and hence the enzyme's activity. This is why these 'negative feedback' regulatory enzymes are termed *allosteric enzymes* as the word allo-steric means 'other site' (see pages 40 and 41).

■ SUMMARY

After reading this chapter you should have some ideas as to how to answer the questions posed in Chapter 1. You could also try to write a biochemical account of metabolism based on the cartoon below which depicts part of the process.

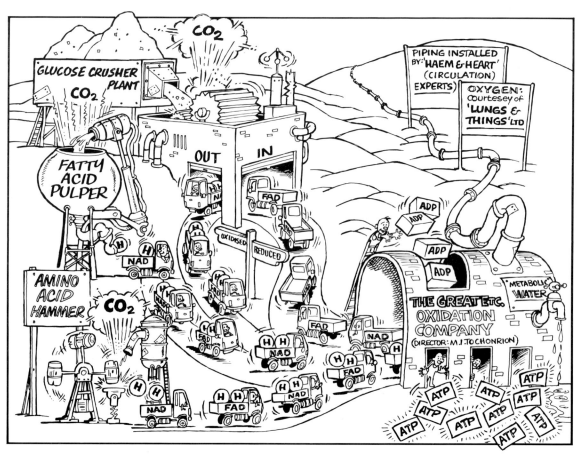

AN INTRODUCTION
TO THE BIOCHEMISTRY
OF AUTOTROPHS

■ INTRODUCTION

This chapter is about plant biochemistry: a topic of both fascination and great importance. Yet, it is not unusual to find that animal biochemistry is more 'popular' with students new to the subject of biochemistry. This is, most probably, because the ideas covered on the animal side of things can so easily be related to ourselves. For example, if you imagine a time when you have exercised to the point that sweat pours from you, Fig. 1.7 (page 10) makes a lot of sense. Heat leaks into the tissues whenever ATP is made or is used – and that excess of heat is carried away by circulating blood to the cooling surfaces of the skin. Similarly, it is biochemically 'obvious' that, during vigorous exercise, the lungs within your panting chest eliminate carbon dioxide and take in oxygen at an enormous rate. The 'carbon dioxide out' arrows of the link reaction and of the Krebs cycle, together with the activity of 'oxygen-hungry' cytochrome a_3 in the electron transport chain, provide an excellent explanation for these common observations of respiratory physiology.

But what of green plants? They effect our lives enormously in several different ways. As you will have seen earlier, plants are the ultimate source of all organic compounds for heterotrophs. They are also the source of specific, essential, organic compounds such as vitamins and some amino acids. It may also be through the photosynthetic power of plants that humans may find some escape from climatic changes associated with the greenhouse effect. Finally, as we shall see in the following section, plants have had an enormous effect on the evolutionary history of our planet's atmosphere.

■ BIOCHEMICAL EVOLUTION

Consider the path of evolution. Life began, as you remember, about 3.6 billion years ago. The shallow seas were full of dissolved organic compounds, the atmosphere was a mixture mainly of nitrogen, carbon dioxide, methane, hydrogen and there was *no oxygen*. This is not merely speculation. Firm geological evidence, mostly centred on the presence of reduced iron [Fe(II)] and the absence of oxidised iron [Fe(III)] in rocks of the period, shows this to be true.

Q What types of organism might have existed in these ancient oxygen-less seas? What types of metabolism might these organisms have had?

They could not have had *aerobic* respiration, for the simple reason that there was no oxygen. In fact the earliest organisms were, almost certainly, primitive anaerobic bacteria. They were prokaryotes (i.e. having no membrane-bound organelles) and they made their ATP by fermenting molecules drawn from the rich organic soup in the sea around them. In short, anaerobic catabolism was almost certainly the earliest ATP-making process in the history of life.

This process of anaerobic catabolism continued for another five hundred million years. These ultra-primitive, totally anaerobic heterotrophic bacteria lived in a world devoid of oxygen, making do with the comparatively tiny yields of ATP. With time, the supplies of geo-organic material (i.e. material produced through atmospheric conditions) would have diminished. Throughout this long period of time, the evolution of larger, multicellular organisms remained impossible in terms of bioenergetics as fermentation is such an inefficient way of liberating energy. However, look carefully now at Fig. 7.1.

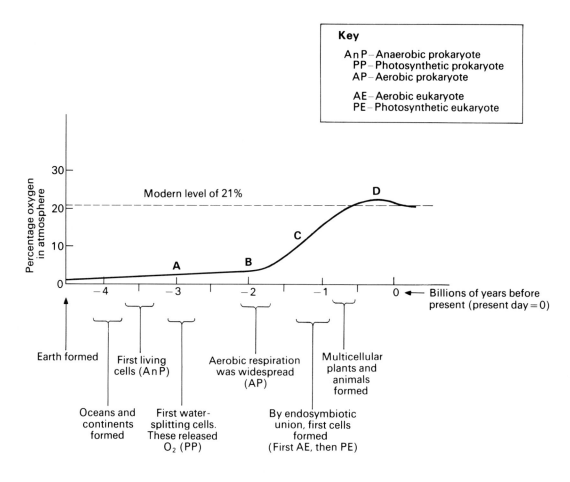

Figure 7.1 Biochemical evolution. Points A, B and C are referred to in the text. Note, in passing, that around point D atmospheric oxygen was probably present in slightly greater concentration than at present (due to the extent of plant cover across the continents). Around this time vertebrates evolved. The term 'endosymbiotic union' is explained in the text.

Around the time marked A in Fig. 7.1 some of these ancient bacteria developed a way of coping with the problem of diminishing supplies of geo-organic compounds. Through evolution, they acquired a method of:

- making ATP from ADP and P_i using the energy from the sun to do it;
- using light energy to split water molecules into oxygen and 'reducing power' in the form of reduced coenzymes. These coenzymes were then used to reduce the abundant supplies of carbon dioxide to organic compounds.

The process involved can be represented as:

$$nADP + nP_i \xrightarrow{\text{Light}} nATP$$

$$2H_2O \xrightarrow{\text{Light}} O_2 + \text{"4H"}$$

$$\text{"4H"} + CO_2 \xrightarrow{nATP} \text{organic compounds}$$

The process is, as you may recognise, *photosynthesis*. Figure 7.1 shows how over the next two billion years oxygen accumulated in the atmosphere. Thus, through the gradual production of oxygen by these ancient photosynthetic bacteria, the atmosphere of the Earth was slowly transformed from having no oxygen to one of comparative oxygen-richness.

The availability of free oxygen in the air opened the door to more evolutionary change. Some of the primitive prokaryotes (i.e. those that had not evolved into photosynthetic bacteria) found ways to abandon anaerobic fermentation and began to make use of the newly available oxygen. The oxygen was used to catabolise organic compounds (perhaps formed from gases of the atmosphere by UV light and lightning or derived from the bodies of green bacteria) in an oxidative way. Point B in Fig. 7.1 marks the time when these 'aerobic' organisms had become widespread.

Q What three main kinds of organism might have existed at point B in Fig. 7.1?

The organisms existing at this time were all marine prokaryotes. Nearly two billion years of evolution had yielded just three groups of ancient bacteria in terms of their method of nutrition, i.e. anaerobic heterotrophs, photosynthetic bacteria and aerobic bacteria. The next step in evolution almost certainly involved a kind of marriage of convenience between two of the existing kinds of organism. Imagine a rather large anaerobic prokaryote living in those ancient seas. Suppose that, because of its particular environment, it has a good supply of organic fuel. What it lacks (because it is a fermenter) is the capacity to make use of *all* the chemical potential energy in that fuel. In some way, however, it engulfed a number of nearby, very small aerobic bacteria which then continued to live inside the host cell. From then on, this package of 'large-cell-containing-many-small-cells' reproduces as a single unit. Living together in this way provides benefits for each cell type. The smaller aerobic 'cells' have a sheltered environment and a good supply of organic material provided by the host. The larger 'cell' has a powerfully oxidative 'ATP-making department' within its cell. With such combined power, the chance of surviving long enough to reproduce is increased. *Symbiosis* is the biological term for this kind of supportive living-together. In this example, one cell is living inside the other and so the name *endosymbiosis* is used.

Q Does the description of what has been formed when the large anaerobic prokaryote engulfs the small aerobic prokaryote remind you of anything? Refer back to Box 6.1 in Chapter 6.

In fact, what has been formed is a eukaryotic cell existing and reproducing as a unicellular aerobic heterotroph. The engulfed bacteria have taken on the role of mitochondria and what was formerly the host cell now provides the cell membrane and the cytoplasm. This is called the *endosymbiont* theory of the origin of mitochondria and happened around the point marked C in Fig. 7.1. There is a good deal of evidence for this theory not least that the mitochondria replicate themselves by division and contain DNA that codes for some of the proteins of the mitochondrial cell's structure.

Also around the point C in Fig. 7.1, or perhaps just a little later, occurred yet another evolutionary landmark. This was the evolution of eukaryotic green cells, i.e. the first unicellular green algae. This can be pictured as happening through the invasion of eukaryotic, aerobic, heterotrophic cells (formed as described in the preceding paragraph) by some of the photosynthetic prokaryotes already existing. This fresh kind of endosymbiosis gave rise to a new type of eukaryote containing both *mitochondria* and *chloroplasts*. Once again, evidence supports this theory, especially in that chloroplasts (like mitochondria) are DNA-containing self-replicating organelles. All of these evolutionary changes are summarised in Fig. 7.2.

Once the eukaryotic cells had formed, the way was open for multicellular organisms to evolve. The reason for this was because both kinds of eukaryotic cell, i.e. plant and animal, could readily produce great quantities of ATP. In both plant and animal cells the energy-transforming processes were confined to specialist organelles thus leaving the outer parts of the cell uncluttered and free to form ordered relationships with other cells. Both the plants and animals were free from the constraints of a limited supply of organic compounds 'left over' from the earliest Earth history. The photoautotrophs were able to use atmospheric (or dissolved) carbon dioxide directly while the heterotrophs were able to 'live off' the huge quantities of autotrophs.

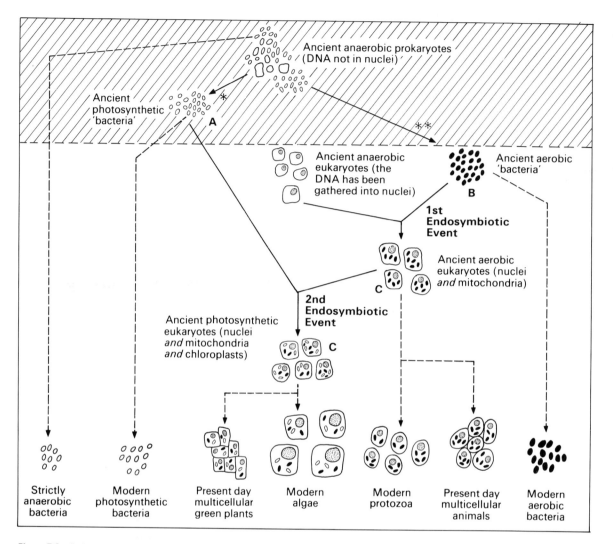

Figure 7.2 Endosymbiotic theory for the evolution of modern eukaryotic organisms. This diagram can be cross-referenced to Figure 7.1 by using the letters A, B and C. In the shaded part of the diagram the atmosphere was essentially reducing. In the unshaded zone, liberation of oxygen by ancient photosynthetic bacteria has created an oxidising atmosphere. Around the period marked * the enzymes of photosynthesis arose by Darwinian evolution; similarly, the enzymes of the electron transport chain evolved around the period marked **.

■ THE ANATOMY OF A GREEN PLANT

Look back at Fig. 1.1 in Chapter 1. Photosynthetic autotrophs occur in three of the five kingdoms. Those with the longest ancient evolutionary lineage are the green and blue-green bacteria of the present day. Apart from these prokaryotes, there are a large number of green unicellular species; single-celled eukaryotes such as *Chlamydomonas* and *Euglena* species are examples you may come across. Biologists frequently group these autotrophs along with heterotrophic protozoa such as amoebae and paramecia in the kingdom of the Protoctists. Then, there are the green multicellular plants, i.e. 'real' plants such as cabbages and pine trees that form the kingdom of the Plantae. In this chapter and the next we will examine the biochemistry of these. Box 7.1 deals briefly with autotrophism in other kingdoms.

■ BOX 7.1 AUTOTROPHISM IN OTHER KINDS OF ORGANISM

You saw on page 8 in Chapter 1 that autotrophic organisms are those that obtain their carbon in the form of CO_2. Although all species in the plant kingdom are autotrophs, the reverse is not true: not all autotrophs are plants. The organisms listed in the following simple classification are briefly described in this Box.

Autotrophs

1. *Chemoautotrophs*
   (i) Certain bacteria

2. *Photoautotrophs*
   (i) Green plants;
   (ii) Algae (in kingdom Protoctista);
   (iii) Cyanobacteria ('blue-green' algae);
   (iv) Sulphur bacteria ('green' and 'purple' bacteria).

Bacteria that are *chemoautotrophs* are chemosynthetic instead of photosynthetic. In other words, although they fix CO_2 to carbohydrate, they do not use light energy to make the ATP necessary for this and other processes. Instead, they obtain their energy by oxidising various kinds of inorganic compound. The precise nature of the oxidation-reduction (redox) reaction that is used varies from species to species. The inorganic 'fuel' may be hydrogen, hydrogen sulphide, carbon monoxide, methane, etc.

Two examples may be familiar from your study of ecology:

● *Nitrosomonas* sp uses molecular oxygen to oxidise ammonium ions (NH_4^+) to nitrite ions (NO_2^-). It uses the energy released to make ATP and hence fix CO_2.
● *Nitrobacter* sp similarly oxidises nitrite to nitrate (NO_3^-).

Both of these chemoautotrophs are ecologically essential. As 'nitrifying' bacteria they have a major role in the nitrogen cycle.

The *photoautotrophs*, of course, use light energy. The algae in the kingdom Protoctista may be unicellular (e.g. *Euglena* sp) or multicellular (e.g. all the seaweeds such as *Fucus* sp). Their biochemistry is very similar to that of green plants. In seaweeds, accessory photosynthetic pigments such as carotenoids and xanthophylls assist normal chlorophyll in absorbing light.

The Cyanobacteria are prokaryotes. Their ancestors (as described in Fig. 7.2) were the first oxygen-producing organisms. They are biochemically similar to plants and green algae. Using light energy, ATP is made from ADP and P_i and water is split (photolysed) into oxygen and 'reducing power'. The ATP and 'reduced power' then convert CO_2 to carbohydrate. Cyanobacteria (such as *Nostoc* sp) have similar chlorophyll to that of plants.

Finally, there is the group of sulphur bacteria. This group sub-divides into the green sulphur bacteria (e.g. *Chlorobium* sp) and purple sulphur bacteria (e.g. *Chromatium* sp). Although these fix CO_2 and use sunlight as their energy source in the production of ATP, they use *sulphur compounds instead of water* in the production of 'reducing power'. This means, of course, that they do not liberate oxygen. Both *Chlorobium* and *Chromatium* can use hydrogen sulphide, H_2S, in this manner and sulphur is released instead of oxygen. The overall equation (which you should compare with the one for green plants on page 95) is:

$$6CO_2 + 12H_2S \longrightarrow C_6H_{12}O_6 + 6H_2O + 12S$$

These bacteria evolved before the oxygen producers in Fig. 7.2. Note that their chlorophyll is different from that of plants and is termed *bacteriochlorophyll*.

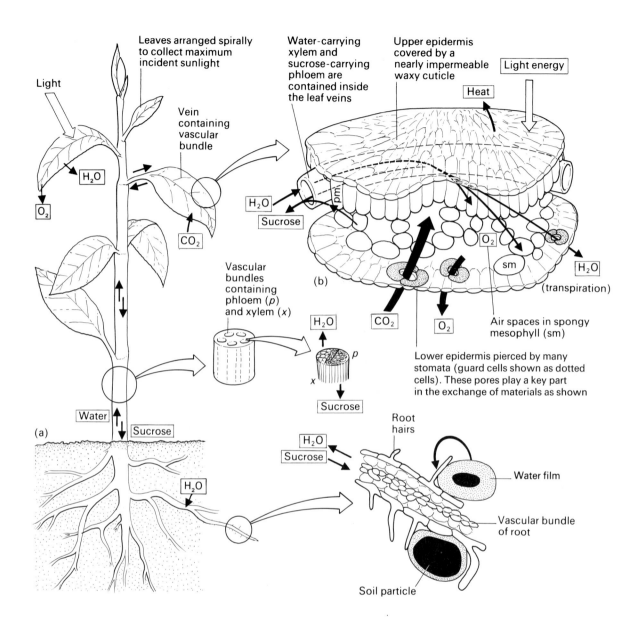

Figure 7.3 (a) The movements of chemicals and energy associated with photosynthesis. Figure 7.3(b) The arrangement of plant tissues is typical of that found in many flowering plants: the *principle*, however, applies to all plants. The 'biochemical factories' of photosynthesis are located in the many chloroplasts within the green cells of the palisade mesophyll and spongy mesophyll in the interior of each leaf cell (pm and sm above). The entire structure of the plant and its physiology can be seen as serving these factories. **Water** enters root hairs by osmosis. Only about 2% is actually used in photosynthesis: the rest is lost by transpiration. **Carbon dioxide** enters the air spaces (30–50% of leaf volume) via the stomata. **Light** passes through the translucent epidermis and a very small fraction (1–2%) is absorbed by the photosynthetic pigments and used to provide energy for photosynthesis. The rest is reflected or used as heat to evaporate water in transpiration. **Oxygen** is either liberated or absorbed depending on the relative rates of respiration and photosynthesis. **Carbohydrate** made by photosynthesis is either temporarily stored as starch grains or transported (translocated) as soluble sucrose. **Heat**, either produced as a biochemical by-product or from light, is re-radiated.

94

Based on what has just been said about evolution, you should be expecting that plants, i.e. multicellular photoautotrophic eukaryotes, will have a fully operative mitochondrial oxidative system and will possess chloroplasts that fix carbon dioxide into organic compounds using ATP and reduced coenzymes. As the mechanism of Darwinian evolution always leads to a close match between structure and function, you may also be expecting the anatomy of a green plant to relate closely to the physiology and biochemistry that go on within that plant. Look now at Fig. 7.3.

In Fig. 7.3(a), you can see the entire plant. Energy from the light striking the blades of the green leaves brings about the conversion of carbon dioxide and water to carbohydrate and, ultimately, to all other organic compounds. In land plants, carbon dioxide from the atmosphere enters the plants through the leaf pores (or *stomata*) and most water enters from the soil via the root hairs. As to the carbohydrate that is formed, the most recognisable immediate product is glucose. Some of this glucose is instantly available for normal carbohydrate catabolism within the leaf cells in exactly the way you have seen in Chapter 6. However, some glucose is also converted to the disaccharide *sucrose* in which form it is carried all over the plant via bundles of conducting cells called *phloem*. Within other cells, possibly very distant from the leaves, the sucrose is reconverted to glucose and the 'great catabolic merry-go-round' starts off. The standard four stages of catabolism break down the glucose providing, as ever, the flood of intracellular ATP and small molecules needed for cell life.

Q Name, in order, the four stages by which plant cells catabolise glucose. Find the answer in the previous chapter if you cannot remember them.

Look now at Fig. 7.3(b) which shows a close-up of the leaf. You can see how water is brought close to the mesophyll cells, which form the interior of the leaf, by the conducting vessels of the *xylem*. In the same vascular bundles, run the phloem tubes that conduct away the sugar products of photosynthesis. The molecules of carbon dioxide diffuse in via the stomata, dissolving in the wet layer on the outside of the mesophyll cells, then penetrating those cells and finally entering the many chloroplasts that fill the cytoplasm and within which photosynthesis occurs.

But before we 'get inside the chloroplast' so to speak, you should remember that there is much more to plant biochemistry than photosynthesis. That this must be the case becomes obvious if you think about it. Plants cells contain amino acids, proteins, fats and oils, nucleic acids, cellulose, pigments such as chlorophyll and carotene, cell wall substances such as pectin, cellulose, hemicelluloses, lignin and so on. All the carbon atoms of this multitude of organic compounds comes from the carbohydrate made photosynthetically. The nitrogen part comes from nitrate ions absorbed through the roots; the sulphur and phosphorus parts come from root absorption of sulphate and phosphate ions. The reshaping of all these components into the huge range of plants products involves dozens of other biochemical pathways which, unfortunately (or fortunately!), are not within the scope of this book.

■ **THE BIOCHEMISTRY OF PHOTOSYNTHESIS: AN OVERALL VIEW**

When glucose is completely catabolised to carbon dioxide, the process is one of oxidation. Not surprisingly, the conversion of carbon dioxide back to glucose is a *reduction*. In simple terms you can think of hydrogen atoms being 'ripped off' the water molecules (leaving behind molecular oxygen) and then being used to reduce carbon dioxide to glucose. The energy to break the H—O bonds in water is provided by the photons of incident sunlight.

Comparing the two processes we have:

Oxidative catabolism

$$C_6H_{12}O_6 + 6CO_2 \longrightarrow 6CO_2 + 6H_2O$$
(2900 kJ energy released)

Photosynthesis

$$6CO_2 + 6H_2O \longrightarrow C_6H_{12}O_6 + 6CO_2$$
(2900 kJ energy taken up)

As you can see, the first reaction is in an overall sense the exact reverse of the second including the direction of energy flow. However, when it comes to the biochemical detail of the two processes, they are totally different.

In the kingdom Plantae, photosynthesis occurs entirely within the chloroplasts and it happens in two linked stages. In order, these are the *light-dependent stage* and the *light-independent stage*. As you may have guessed from the name, the various reactions of the light-dependent stage will only occur when the chloroplasts are bathed in light of sufficient intensity (and of the right mix of wavelengths). In contrast, the light-independent stage consists entirely of reactions that do not directly depend on light. Sometimes these two stages are referred to as the 'light stage' and 'dark stage'. However, the latter is a rather misleading term, as you will see shortly.

Before we look at these two stages in more detail and examine how they are linked, you will need to know about the internal structure of chloroplasts (so look now at Fig. 7.4). This set of more and more magnified drawings, working down from cells to molecules, is fairly self-explanatory. There are some new terms in the caption and you should pay particular attention to *stroma, grana* and *thylakoid discs*. Note also that (i) the light dependent stage occurs in the grana and (ii) the light independent stage occurs in the stroma. Stage (d) of Fig. 7.4 will mean more to you shortly.

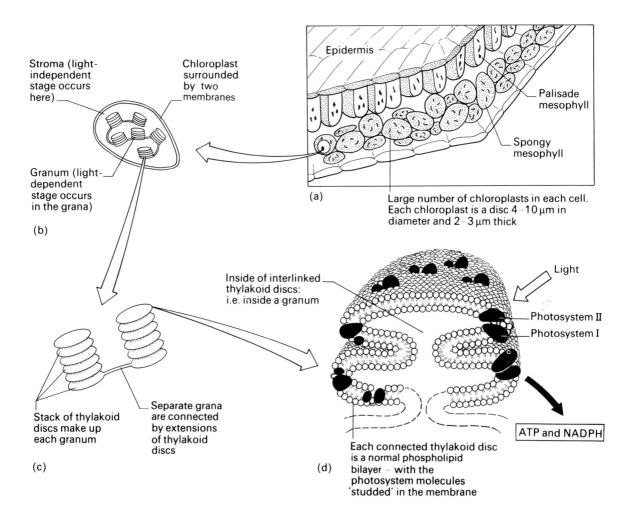

Figure 7.4 Photosynthesis — cells to molecules. Begin by relating (a) to Figure 7.3. Next, carefully note and remember the locations of the light-dependent and light-independent stages shown in (b). In (c), note that each thylakoid disc is connected to all others. In (d), note the membrane that makes up the thylakoid discs is very similar to a cell membrane (page 23). It has the extra molecules of photosystems I and II studded into it.

In the light-dependent stage, light energy is absorbed by chlorophyll and other pigments. This energy, by means of enzymes inside each chloroplast, brings about the photolysis of water. As the very structure of the word suggests ('photo' and 'lysis'), the light splits water molecules so producing oxygen gas and quantities of the reduced coenzyme *NADPH*. The light energy also makes quantities of ATP from ADP and P_i. All the reactions of the light-dependent stage occur inside the thylakoid membranes of the grana. Inside each sheet of thylakoid membrane are found all the molecules of chlorophyll, enzymes and cofactors that are involved in the light-dependent stage. Look back at Fig. 7.4(d) to get an idea of this. The overall reaction of the light-dependent stage is shown in Box A. The significance of the numbers of molecules made (18ATP and 12NADPH) becomes clear shortly.

$$18ADP + 18P_i \xrightarrow{\text{Light}} 18ATP$$

$$12NADP^+ + 12H_2O \xrightarrow{\text{Light}} 12NADPH + 12H^+ + 6O_2$$

Box A These reactions occur in the light-dependent stage and take place in the thylakoid membranes of the grana.

The light-independent stage makes direct and almost immediate use of the products of the light stage to convert carbon dioxide to glucose. As you have just learnt, none of the many reactions of this complicated process requires light. However, they do require the products of the light-dependent stage – thus this second stage does not occur to any significant extent in the dark. This is why the term 'dark-stage' is rather misleading. By means of the reducing power of the NADPH and of the chemical energy available in ATP, carbon dioxide obtained from air, or from water in aquatic plants, is converted to carbohydrate. All the reactions of this second stage take place in the stroma of chloroplasts. The overall reaction of the light-independent stage is shown in Box B.

As you can see from Box B, 12NADPH and 18ATP are needed to make each glucose molecule or, put another way, 2NADPH and 3ATP are needed for each carbon dioxide molecule fixed.

$$12NADPH/H^+ + 18ATP + 6CO_2 \longrightarrow C_6H_{12}O_6 + 6H_2O + 12NADP^+ + 18ADP + 18P_i$$

Box B This reaction occurs in the light-independent stage and takes place in the stroma of the grana.

Now you can add together the two boxes to give the overall equation for photosynthesis. The ATP, ADP, P_i, $NADP^+$, NADPH, and H^+ do not appear in the overall equation simply because, if you think about it, they cancel out when the equations are added.

$$6CO_2 + 6H_2O \longrightarrow C_6H_{12}O_6 + 6O_2$$

Box C The overall process, therefore, involves both the thylakoid membranes and the stroma.

It is important to know these boxed equations and to be able to reproduce the simple ideas shown in Fig. 7.5. There is a *net* consumption of six water molecules and you should note the production of oxygen. This process released oxygen to the atmosphere in the first place.

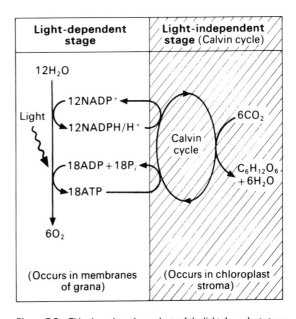

Figure 7.5 This shows how the products of the light-dependent stage of photosynthesis (NADPH/H^+ and ATP) are used in the light-independent stage to convert CO_2 to carbohydrate. The sequence of reactions that makes up the light-independent stage is called the **Calvin cycle**.

■ THE LIGHT-DEPENDENT STAGE: A CLOSER LOOK

You should recall that atoms consist of negatively charged electrons orbiting a positively charged nucleus (see Appendix). When energy is taken into an atom, one or more electrons are promoted (*excited* is the correct term) to orbitals that are further out and hence more energetic. Because only certain orbitals are possible, only certain sized 'packets' of energy can be absorbed. If that energy is light energy, it follows that only light of certain wavelengths can be absorbed by a given compound containing particular atoms. If enough energy is put in, an electron may become so excited that it temporarily leaves the molecule which consequently has a positive charge.

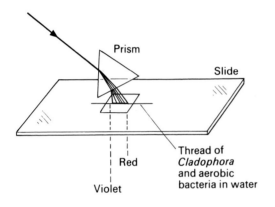

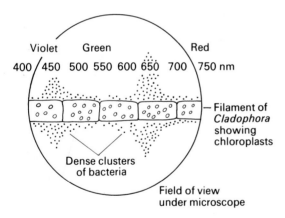

(a) Engelmann used a small prism to project a micro-spectrum of light onto a thread of alga on the slide. Oxygen-loving motile bacteria (*Pseudomonas sp*) congregated in the coloured zones where oxygen production was greatest.

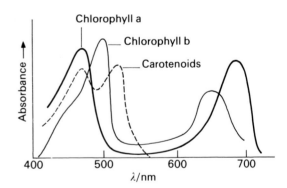

(b) More sophisticated experimentation gives a plot showing rate of photosynthesis against wavelength (λ). This kind of graph is described as a **photosynthetic action spectrum**.

(c) Photosynthesis is driven by energy obtained from the absorbed quanta of light. Not surprisingly, the peaks of maximum absorption correspond to the most effective wavelengths for promoting photosynthesis.

Figure 7.6 (a) Engelmann's experiment, (b) a photosynthetic action spectrum and (c) the absorption spectra for chlorophylls a and b and the carotenoid accessory pigments.

The facts just described lie at the heart of the explanation of how the photosynthetic pigments, such as chlorophyll and others, are able to capture light energy and use it to make NADPH and ATP.

First of all, it is important to realise that only certain wavelengths in the mixture of wavelengths that form white light are photosynthetically useful to plants. Common sense and basic physics tells us which light is *not* useful. Plants look green when viewed in white light because they absorb some wavelengths and reflect back all the unused green wavelengths. A reasonable guess, from this alone, is that perhaps red and blue are useful.

In 1882, Engelmann put a filament of the green alga *Cladophora* in a rainbow patch of light created by putting a prism in the path of a beam of white light. Thus, he was able to illuminate different parts of the long filament with different colours. The way he detected active photosynthesis was ingenious; he added to the medium bacteria of the kind that seek out oxygen. Where they congregated, photosynthesis was active. You can see his results in Fig. 7.6 (a). Wavelengths in the red and blue are indeed involved.

In later and more precise experiments, biochemists measured the rate of photosynthesis at a range of wavelengths. These rates when plotted against wavelength give what is called a *photosynthetic action spectrum*. The shape of this spectrum for ordinary green plants matches very well the shape of the absorption spectrum for the two types of chlorophyll found in those plants (i.e. chlorophylls a and b). Parts (b) and (c) of Fig. 7.6 show this match. If you take the range of plants as a whole, the scene is more complicated than this. Many plants have pigments in addition to chlorophylls a and b. These *accessory photosynthetic pigments* help harvest light of other wavelengths. The carotenoid pigments of seaweeds and some higher plants are just one example. The dotted lines on Fig. 7.6 (c) show how these pigments absorb light of different wavelengths.

Details of how absorbed light is utilised in energy production are complicated and you should extract what you need from the following already very simplified account. There are two separate light-powered systems in the membranes of the thylakoid disc. One of them, which involves *photosystem I*, makes only ATP. The other, which involves both *photosystem I* and *photosystem II*, make both ATP and NADPH. The best way to understand what is going on is to look at Fig. 7.7 (a) and (b), try to work it out, read the points below carefully, then look again at the figures.

(a)

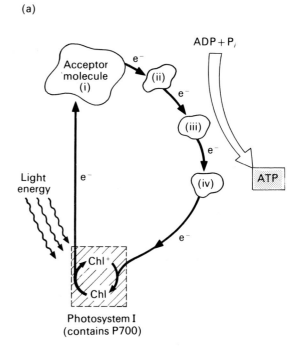

(a) Cyclic photophosphorylation. ATP is the only product. Molecules (i) → (iv) form an electron transport chain that is different in detail, but similar in principle to the ETC in mitochondria. ATP is made as a consequence of electron flow. The chlorophyll molecule at the centre of PSI is P700 (absorbing light of that wavelength). It is surrounded by molecules of chlorophylls a and b. All these molecules are 'studded into' the membranes of the grana.

Figure 7.7 The light stage of photosynthesis. Your syllabus may well not require all this detail, but the background explanation will help you to understand the simpler ideas.

(b)

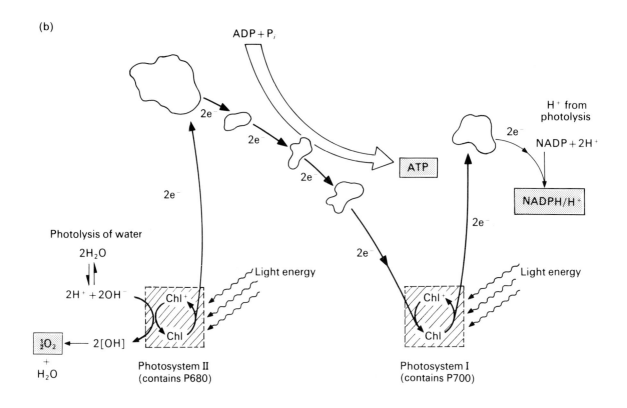

Figure 7.7 (b) Non-cyclic photophosphorylation. The products are in shaded boxes. Note that the $2H^+$ produced by the splitting of water (bottom left) are involved (top right) in the production of $NADP/H^+$. PSII contains another special chlorophyll, P680 (absorbing light of that wavelength). Once again, many molecules of chlorophylls a and b are also present.

■ CYCLIC PHOTOPHOSPHORYLATION

Let's take the scheme for cyclic photophophorylation first. This is easier to understand as it does not involve water, does not make oxygen and does not make NADPH. In fact all it does is to make ATP from ADP and P_i using light energy to bring about this otherwise very endergonic reaction. On and within the thylakoid membrane are many 'clusters' of molecules, each cluster making up photosystem I. Each cluster contains several hundred chlorophyll molecules, i.e. a mixture of mainly chlorophyll a but with some chlorophyll b. Light falls on the cluster and excites the electrons in all the molecules present. The energy of those many excited electrons is 'funnelled'

to one special chlorophyll molecule, i.e. the *reaction centre* of the cluster. In cyclic photophosphorylation, that reaction centre molecule is called chlorophyll P700. This one molecule becomes so energised that an *electron actually leaves the molecule and is collected by an electron acceptor*. This means, of course, the chlorophyll at the reaction centre is positively charged and the acceptor is now reduced. All that happens now is that the electron leaves the acceptor and passes down a series of electron-carriers *back* to the positively charged chlorophyll P700 molecule in the reaction centre (see Fig. 7.7(a)).

In fact, what we have here (if you cast your mind back to the description of the ETC in Chapter 5) is another kind of electron transport chain but this time in the chloroplasts instead of in the mitochondria. The precise identity of the components is different but the principle is exactly the same, i.e. the passage of electrons down a series of redox carriers leading to the production of ATP. And, of course, the return of the electron to the positively charged chlorophyll molecule gives us back an uncharged molecule. The significance of the words 'cyclic', 'photo' and 'phosphorylation' in the overall term should now be clear.

■ NON-CYCLIC PHOTOPHOSPHORYLATION

Once you have got the idea of cyclic photophosphorylation, then non-cyclic photophosphorylation is not particularly hard to understand, even though it is more complicated. In this case, water is involved (it undergoes photolysis), oxygen is produced, $NADPH/H^+$ is formed, and ATP is produced. In addition, photosystem II as well as photosystem I is involved. The special reaction centre chlorophyll molecule in photosystem II is called P690. The scheme (sometimes called the 'Z scheme' for the obvious reason) can be slightly confusing to remember. Note that in Fig. 7.7(b) photosystem II appears on the left-hand side of the diagram. Thus, the numbering of the sequence of reactions is the reverse of what we might have expected.

The sequence is as follows. Water (H_2O) ionises to give a H^+ ion and a OH^- ion. Meanwhile, photosystem II has been so energised by incident light that it emits an electron and the reaction centre temporarily becomes positive. The positively charged chlorophyll molecule (Chl^+) immediately reacts with the OH^- ion of water giving back an uncharged chlorophyll molecule and an unstable, uncharged [OH]. An [OH] instantly combines with an [OH] made in the same way to give back some water and oxygen gas. The numbers get quite complicated and you may well not want to try and deal with them. In fact the reaction is:

$$4H_2O \rightleftharpoons 4H^+ + 4OH^-$$

$$4OH^- \longrightarrow 4[OH] + 4e^-$$

$$4[OH] \longrightarrow 2H_2O + O_2$$

Overall: $\quad 2H_2O \longrightarrow O_2 + 4H^+ + 4e^-$

However, the main points to note are that at this stage water has been photolysed and oxygen has been made and four electrons have been released.

The plant now has these four high-powered electrons to do things with! In fact, once again these are collected by electron acceptors and allowed to flow down an electron transport chain, so making ATP by photophosphorylation. In this case, however, the electrons do *not* go back to the reaction centre of photosystem II (it is already electrically neutral thanks to OH^- ion). Instead, they are re-energised with more light energy at photosystem I and are collected afresh by another electron acceptor. They are then passed on to the awaiting $NADP^+$ molecules and these are reduced to NADPH.

In fact, we have:

$$2NADP^+ + 4H^+ + 4e^- \longrightarrow 2NADPH/H^+$$

Where did these H^+ ions come from? The answer is from water photolysis. We had $4H^+$ produced from the splitting of two water molecules which leaves us with $2H^+$ left over so that we can write an overall equation as shown in Box D.

$$2NADP^+ + 2H_2O \longrightarrow 2NADPH/H^+ + O_2$$

Box D

One point to note is that the mechanism of photophosphorylation is very similar to that of oxidative phosphorylation. You learnt in Box 6.2 of Chapter 6 that, in oxidative phosphorylation, ATP is made by allowing hydrogen ions, produced as a consequence of electron transport, to build up on the outside of the inner mitochondrial membrane – and then to flow back into the cytoplasm *down a gradient of concentration and charge*. The osmotic work thus made available is coupled to ATP manufacture. In both cyclic and non-cyclic photophosphorylation, a similar thing happens: as a consequence of electron transport, hydrogen ions build up in the *inside* of the thylakoid disc (note the difference between chloroplasts and mitochondria) and a gradient is therefore produced. As the H^+ ions flow out of the disc, ATP is made (see Fig. 7.8).

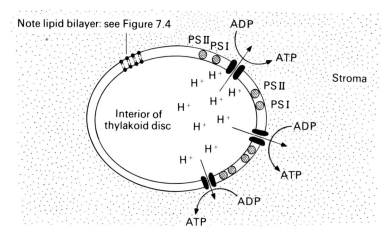

Figure 7.8 The mechanism of photosynthesis. As electron transport occurs (in both cyclic and non-cyclic photophosphorylation) a build-up of H^+ ions occurs inside the stack of thylakoid discs that make up each granum. These hydrogen ions flow out and *down* a gradient of both concentration and electrical potential difference, and ATP is made as a consequence. (Note that in mitochondria the build up of H^+ is outside the mitochondrial membrane.)

■ THE LIGHT-INDEPENDENT STAGE: AN UNUSUAL LOOK

Put yourself in the role of an atmospheric carbon dioxide (CO_2) molecule. At present, there are about 330 molecules of CO_2 per million of the other kinds of molecule found in air – nitrogen, oxygen, etc. By entirely passive diffusion, you enter the sub-stomatal space of a leaf. The reason why there is a net flow of CO_2 molecules in that direction is because CO_2 molecules are being used up by the mesophyll cells. This produces a lower concentration of CO_2 in the intercellular spaces than in the atmosphere, thus creating a concentration gradient that permits this diffusion. Once inside the leaf, you dissolve in the film of water on the outside of a spongy mesophyll cell.

You then penetrate the plasma membrane of the nearest cell or, possibly, you follow the dissolved CO_2 concentration gradient and move in the water film between cells to penetrate some more distant mesophyll cell. Once inside the cytoplasm, the concentration gradient has become greater and you are drawn strongly towards a huge green organelle, i.e. the nearest chloroplast. You pass through the outer membrane then the inner membrane and find yourself in a rather thick matrix which is full of dissolved proteins. The matrix is the *stroma* and the proteins are the enzymes of the light-independent stage. These enzymes make up the CO_2-fixing sequence known as

the *Calvin cycle*. You are now in the last few moments of your existence as an independent CO_2 molecule. As the reactions catalysed by the enzymes of the Calvin cycle begin, you are converted step by step through a range of intermediates – joining with the other molecules derived from other CO_2 molecules until you finally become part of a glucose molecule.

What we term photosynthesis is now complete. Your journey, however, is not. You may be metabolically transformed (joining with other molecules as necessary) into sucrose, amylose, amylopectin, cellulose, fat droplets, alanine, glycine, DNA, RNA and so on. You may, however, remain as glucose and be rapidly respired, by glycolysis and the reactions within a mitochondrion. If so, you will re-emerge rapidly as CO_2 again. Or you may remain as cellulose or lignin and be trapped as a fragment of wood for the next ten thousand years!

This 'soap-opera' way of presenting biochemistry is not a style which one should present in examination essays. Nevertheless, as private, imaginative thinking, it is sometimes a useful way of understanding and remembering. However, returning to a more formal style, let us consider what reaction in the Calvin cycle actually captures CO_2 and then what happens afterwards. Look carefully at Fig. 7.9 then return to the text for explanations.

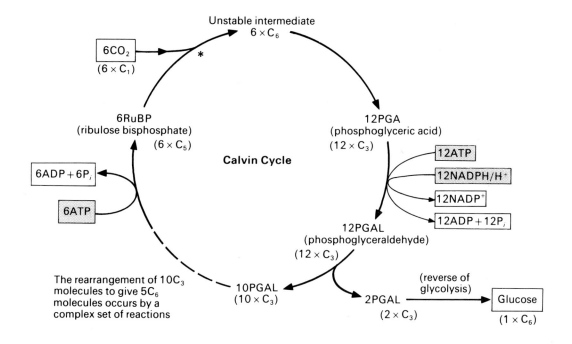

Figure 7.9 Details of the Calvin cycle. The diagram shows how $6CO_2$ (top left) are converted to one molecule of glucose (bottom right). The products of the light-dependent stage, ATP and NADPH/H$^+$, are used as shown in the shaded boxes. The reaction marked by the asterisk is the initial CO_2-fixation reaction and is catalysed by the enzyme *ribulose bisphosphate carboxylase*. The very many enzymes of the Calvin cycle are located in solution in the stroma of the chloroplasts.

■ THE CALVIN CYCLE

Look at the asterisk in Fig. 7.9. This is the starting point, i.e. the reaction that fixes CO_2. In this reaction, the energy rich compound ribulose bisphosphate (RuBP) combines with CO_2 to produce an unstable compound containing six carbon atoms that immediately breaks down into two molecules of phosphoglyceric acid (PGA) each of which has three carbon atoms.

$$C_5 + CO_2 \longrightarrow {}'C_6' \longrightarrow 2 \times C_3$$

The enzyme that catalyses the reaction is called *ribulose bisphosphate carboxylase*. This is so named because it carboxylates (meaning 'puts CO_2 into') its substrate RuBP. Interestingly RuBP carboxylase accounts for about half the mass of all leaf protein and, as there are so many leaves, there is more of this enzyme on the planet than any other!

Six CO_2 molecules (reacting with 6RuBP molecules) therefore yield 12PGA which, following reduction by 12NADPH assisted by 12ATP (all produced in the light-dependent stage), are converted to 12phosphoglyceraldehyde (PGAL). This conversion is just like part of the glycolytic pathway in reverse, except that the coenzyme in the Calvin cycle is NADP not NAD.

Why 'bisphosphate' and not 'disphosphate'? In ADP, the two phosphate groups are attached to each other. In RuBP, the 'bis' tells us that each of the two phosphate groups is joined to a different part of the molecule.

PGA is now often written as GP which stands for glycerate-3-phosphate. In the same way, PGAL may be written as GALP which stands for glyceraldehyde-3-phosphate!

What happens now is that *two* of those PGAL molecules go on to make glucose and the other ten go on to remake the 6RuBP that are required to fix another $6CO_2$ molecules. (This latter stage is a very complicated one, the unscrambling of which earned Calvin the Nobel prize.) You should note that another 6ATP are required to do this reconversion.

$$2 \times C_3 \longrightarrow C_6 \text{ (glucose)}$$

$$10 \times C_3 \longrightarrow 6 \times C_5 \text{ (RuBP)}$$

In most courses of study you will not need all the detail given here. However, by reasoning the text through carefully, along with Fig. 7.9, you should be able to understand what is happening and so be confident about the shortened version of the Calvin cycle in Fig. 7.9. Test your understanding with this question.

Q To make one glucose molecule, $(12+6)$ATP and 12NADPH are needed. What relative contributions to the supply of these is made by the cyclic and noncyclic photophosphorylation processes of the light-dependent stage?

Non-cyclic photophosphorylation makes ATP and NADPH in a 1:1 ratio, i.e. it will make the 12ATP and 12NADPH. It is cyclic photophosphorylation that has to make up the deficit, i.e. the other 6ATP.

■ RESPIRATION IN PLANTS

There is not a great deal need be said about this as the biochemical processes are similar to those in animals. The actual rate of respiration (per unit mass of tissue) is much lower in plants, i.e. generally around a tenth of that in animals. This you would very much expect as they live a life fixed in one position by their roots and are entirely without muscles. However, respiration does occur and is essential. Though a few energy-requiring processes within leaves could make direct use of photosynthetically produced ATP, very few in fact do and leaf cells contain mitochondria as well as chloroplasts. Certainly in all cells that do not contain chloroplasts (the root system and the inside of stems, for

example) ATP can *only* be made available through respiration. The cells of a plant in a dark box are just like those of an animal!

Q Can you remember (or work out) which will be the main energy-requiring process in plants? Compare your list with the following text.

There are just two processes. These are:

● ATP usage in biosynthesis;
● ATP usage in the active transport of ions and molecules.

As ever, heat will be leaked in the ATP-making and ATP-using steps, but (unlike animals) this is a small, slowly produced amount. An exception is when plants are metabolically very active, e.g. when seeds are germinating. A simple experiment demonstrates that when wet peas are put into a thermos flask with a thermometer through the bung, by the next day a measurable temperature rise has usually occurred.

The idea of germinating seeds serves to introduce the two final points of this section. Firstly, we need to realise that plants, like animals, are able to catabolise nutrients other than glucose. Many seeds contain large amounts of fat often in the form of oil droplets. (We harvest certain seeds for their oil, e.g. sunflower oil, groundnut oil, sesame seed oil and corn oil.) These reserves provide the energy store for the growing seedlings, 'keeping them going' until they begin to photosynthesise and are thus able to lead an existence independent of the food store. In other seeds, glucose polymers (straight-chained amylose and branch-chained amylopectin) provide the necessary food storage compounds. Some seeds store large amounts of protein and from Chapter 5 you may remember that the pulses, i.e. peas, beans, etc. are examples of these.

Secondly, the 'wet pea' experiment mentioned above reminds us that plants are also able to respire anaerobically. This does not happen a great deal as a plant's oxygen supply is usually good and its needs for oxygen is generally small. However, when a plant is very active and the oxygen supply is inadequate, fermentations of the type discussed in the last chapter can occur, in particular alcoholic fermentation. If you uncork the germinating 'wet pea' flask and sniff, the smell of ethanol is usually quite strong.

PLANT BIOCHEMISTRY: SOME OTHER ASPECTS

■ INTRODUCTION

The previous chapter explained how the majority of green plants capture solar energy, carbon dioxide and water and generate from these the numerous compounds of which plants are made. Even in Fig. 8.1, we are reminded that the carbohydrate products of the Calvin cycle, i.e. PGAL, glucose-6-phosphate, and glucose itself, are converted to other things. The starch grains and oil droplets in the chloroplast stroma are evidence of this. Similarly, carbon dioxide passing into the stomata and entering the Calvin cycle becomes incorporated into amino acids in just 60 seconds. Within five minutes proteins and many other cellular organic chemicals contain carbon atoms from that carbon dioxide.

In this chapter we shall cover the biochemical regulation of the Calvin cycle, the slightly different methods of photosynthesis adopted by temperate and some tropical plants (including *en route* a strange phenomenon called photorespiration), links with plant physiology and, finally, a note on nitrogen fixation.

■ PHOTOSYNTHESIS: A QUESTION OF METABOLIC CONTROL

As you will see later, there are several rather large-scale effects that influence the rate at which plants create new organic compounds from carbon dioxide and water. Sufficient light and an adequate supply of carbon dioxide are both essential requirements for photosynthesis. Depending on the species of plant, one or other of these two factors is normally the *rate limiting step*. However, at the very heart of the photosynthetic process is the enzymatic machinery inside the chloroplast, and we should expect to find some regulatory mechanism at the molecular level, i.e. some sort of link-up between light, carbon dioxide and what the enzymes do.

You last met the idea of regulatory enzymes in Chapter 6, where we looked briefly into one of the enzymes of glycolysis, i.e. phosphofructokinase (PFK). There, you learned that the activity of this regulatory enzyme is 'turned up' or 'turned down' depending on the metabolic needs of the cell. The same principle applies in leaf mesophyll cells. This time, however, the regulatory enzyme is ribulose biphosphate carboxylase (RuBP carboxylase). As you know, this catalyses the reaction

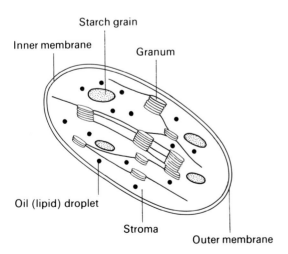

$$\text{Ribulose bisphosphate} + CO_2 \xrightarrow{\textit{RuBP carboxylase}} \text{unstable 'C}_6\text{'} \longrightarrow 2PGA$$

Box A

Figure 8.1 Simplified diagram of a chloroplast showing accumulation of starch grains and oil droplets.

When the leaves are bathed in light and, therefore, plenty of NADPH and ATP is being made, it is important to the plant that the 'CO$_2$-fixing' enzyme should work with maximum efficiency, so that every bit of CO$_2$ can be scavenged from the sub-stomatal airspaces and converted into carbohydrate. Equally, it is important that as soon as the light fades the enzyme should become inactive. If it did not, the Calvin cycle would 'struggle on' until cellular ATP and NADPH fell to very low levels. This would, in turn, make impossible the regeneration of ribulose biphosphate. The chloroplast would, therefore, be in a poor state to restart the processes of photosynthesis when morning sunlight returned. All in all, there needs to be a quick RuBP carboxylase 'switch-off' as soon as it begins to get dark.

There is! It is achieved simply and elegantly by three related processes:

● NADPH is an allosteric activator of RuBP carboxylase. Look back at page 88 if you need to check the meaning of this term. In this case, NADPH formed by photosystem I (in conjunction with photosystem II) binds to the protein of the carboxylase enzyme and, as a consequence of this binding, increases its catalytic power. Thus, more light more NADPH and more RuBP carboxylase activity;

● RuBP carboxylase activity depends on the pH and is much more active at pH 9 than pH 7. You saw in Chapter 7 (look back at Fig. 7.8) that H$^+$ ions accumulate inside the thylakoid discs during the light stage of photosynthesis. The accumulation of H$^+$ *inside* means that they are progressively removed from the stroma *outside* the thylakoid discs. So, of course, the pH in this outer region gradually rises, leading to an increase in RuBP carboxylase activity. When there is no light, there is no concentration of H$^+$ inside the grana (the reverse of the situation above) and the pH of the stroma decreases leading to a fall in RuBP carboxylase activity;

● As H$^+$ ions accumulate inside the grana (in the way described in (ii)), Mg^{2+} ions pass out. This 'charge-balancing exchange' leads to a high Mg^{2+} concentration in the stroma and . . .

Q You should be able to work out 'the biochemical rationale' of it . . . Do you think that RuBP carboxylase will be *activated* or *inhibited* by magnesium ions?

The answer is that it is activated. Thus, lots of light, lots of Mg^{2+} ions in the stroma, lots of carboxylase activity and lots of CO$_2$ fixation.

■ SOME DIFFERENCES BETWEEN PLANTS

The inner core of metabolic control described in the previous section is similar in all higher plants. However, in terms of some of the biochemical processes *associated* with the Calvin cycle, there are some intriguing differences between different species of plants. And, as you will see shortly, these differences amount to evolutionary adaptation at the molecular level.

In terms of the way they assimilate carbon dioxide, biochemists classify plants into three groups:

● C$_3$ plants;
● C$_4$ plants;
● CAM plants.

The first group contains the great bulk of plants in the temperate parts of the world, the typical plants of northern Europe for example. The description C$_3$ simply refers to the fact that the first recognisable compound formed after CO$_2$ fixation contains three carbon atoms. You should be able to recall from earlier pages that this is phosphoglyceric acid (PGA). Check the equation in Box A if you are uncertain. Note that 'unstable C$_6$' is not counted as a recognisable compound.

Photo 8.1   Wheat – a C$_3$ plant.

Photo 8.2 Maize – a C_4 plant.

Photo 8.3 Prickly pear cactus – a CAM plant.

It turns out that not all plants capture CO_2 from the atmosphere by means of this reaction. Many plants that are normally found in hotter regions, sugar cane and maize for example, have a different mechanism of CO_2 capture. In these cases, the first recognisable product of CO_2-fixation is not PGA but is a compound with four carbon atoms per molecule. This C_4 compound, called malic acid, gives the title to this C_4 group. (In fact, as the next section describes, the CO_2 that has been captured within the C_4 molecule is soon passed to ribulose bisphosphate and on into the normal Calvin cycle. As you will see, this method of

CO_2 capture is a major and very elegant evolutionary adaptation to hotter environments.)

What about CAM plants? The letters CAM are the initials of **C**rassulacean **A**cid **M**etabolism. The *Crassulaceae* are just one of several families of plants that belong to the much larger group known loosely as the *succulents*. And, as you may know, the succulents are commonly grouped together with yet another large group of plants, i.e. the cacti. This varied collection of plants are mostly *xerophytes*. This term means that they 'like' (i.e. are able to live successfully in) very dry and often hot environments. They owe much of this success to the fact that they have a method of capturing CO_2 that is very similar (but not quite identical) to the C_4 method outlined above. Plant biochemists first discovered the mechanism in the Crassulaceae. They also noted the involvement of *malic acid*, hence the term Crassulacean *Acid* Metabolism.

■ CARBON DIOXIDE FIXATION IN C_4 PLANTS

To understand why plants have evolved alternative ways of fixing carbon dioxide depends on understanding a peculiar phenomenon called *photorespiration*. A brief outline of this is given in Box 8.1. The key point to note is that, when the 'inside-the-chloroplast' concentration of oxygen is high compared with that of CO_2, the process of photorespiration can 'burn off' large amounts of the carbohydrate that has been so usefully made by photosynthesis. The sketch in Box 8.1 illustrates the wastefulness of this burn off.

Photorespiration is not a particular problem in cooler regions with lower light intensity. In these conditions, the rate of photorespiration is low and RuBP carboxylase is able to act as a carboxylase more effectively than as an oxygenase. As a result, the simple, straightforward C_3 system operates.

However, when it is hot and bright (picture a sugar cane under the Jamaican sun) the rate of photorespiration *would* be devastatingly high *if* RuBP carboxylase were allowed to come into contact with oxygen. In fact, by an ingenious alliance between biochemistry and plant anatomy, this eventuality is prevented. Figure 8.2, together with its caption, summarises the essential points of this alliance.

■ BOX 8.1   PHOTORESPIRATION

In bright sunlight a series of reactions in each chloroplast brings about this overall reaction:

$$\text{Carbohydrate} + O_2 \longrightarrow CO_2$$

The process is termed *photorespiration* and, from the point of view of the plant, is thoroughly undesirable. In some circumstances, as much as 50% of the carbohydrate made by the Calvin cycle is reconverted to CO_2. As this sketch shows, the two routes together are the biochemical equivalent of going upstairs and falling down again.

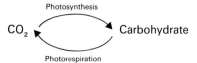

Leaving aside the relatively unimportant biochemical detail the key points to note are that (i) photorespiration has nothing at all to do with the important ATP-making respiration that occurs in plant mitochondria, and (ii) the key step of the several stages of photorespiration is catalysed by ribulose bisphosphate carboxylase (RuBP carboxylase) as shown below.

The oxidising step shown below involves molecular oxygen and, remarkably, is catalysed by the *same enzyme*, RuBP carboxylose, that has such an important role in the Calvin cycle. In the latter, the enzyme acts usefully as a carboxylase whereas in photorespiration it acts harmfully as an oxygenase*. A principal factor that determines *which way* the enzyme acts is the ratio of the concentrations of CO_2 and of O_2 inside the chloroplast.

● If chloroplast CO_2 concentration is high, Calvin cycle activity predominates.
● If chloroplast O_2 concentration is high, photorespiration predominates.

The question of why evolution has left plants with such a peculiar CO_2-fixing enzyme is much debated. Most probably the unwanted oxygenase activity is a remnant of evolutionary history rather like the appendix in humans. In this case, however, the 'remnant' is actively harmful. This is why many plants in hot sunny environments have evolved a special biochemical and structural arrangement that overcomes this difficulty. These are the C_4 plants.

* An oxygenase is an enzyme that catalyses an oxidation involving molecular oxygen.

$$\text{Carbohydrate} \xrightarrow{\text{Glycolysis}} \text{PGA} \longrightarrow \text{RuBP} \xrightarrow[+O_2]{\textit{RuBP carboxylase}} \text{various products} \rightarrow CO_2$$

There is a 'price' to be paid by plants that use C_4 pathway (also called the Hatch–Slack pathway after the names of its principal discoverers). Both ATP and NADPH/H$^+$ are consumed in the malic acid recycling process, thus the C_4 addition to the normal Calvin cycle is energy inefficient. Evolution always

favours the most effective features (whether structural, physiological or biochemical) for a given environment. This explains why the C_3 system gives 'best overall value' in temperate climates whereas the C_4 system has the advantage in hotter, sunnier lands.

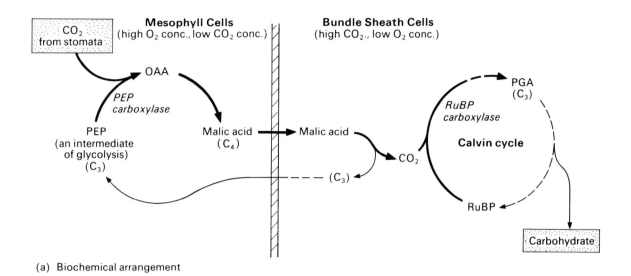

(a) Biochemical arrangement

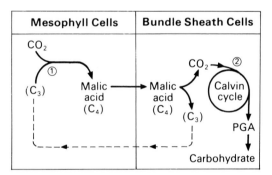

(b) A simplified diagram of C₄ metabolism. Carboxylases act at ① and ②

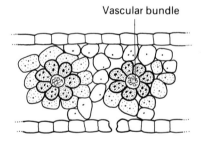

(C) Typical C₄ plant leaf structure. Note the sheath bundle cells (shaded) packed in wreath-like rings around vascular bundles. (This is known as **Kranz Anatomy** – a double ring of cells around the vascular bundle

Figure 8.2 CO_2 fixation in C_4 plants. CO_2 entering stomata is initially captured by combination with a C_3 compound to give a C_4 compound. The catalysing enzyme, *PEP carboxylase*, is not affected by O_2 concentration. The initial C_4 compound is converted to another C_4 compound called malic acid. This is then transported to bundle sheath cells where it re-forms CO_2 and a C_3 compound. The latter is recycled for use in the mesophyll cells but the CO_2 is fixed by RuBP carboxylase into the normal reactions of the Calvin cycle. As O_2 concentration is low and CO_2 concentration is very high inside the sheath cells, little or no photorespiration occurs. [Enthusiasts may note that PEP is phosphoenolpyruvic acid (see Figure 6.5, page 73). OAA is oxaloacetic acid. This, like malic acid is a Krebs cycle intermediate (see Figure 6.6, page 76). Realists, with syllabus and examinations in mind, should learn the simplified version in (b)!]

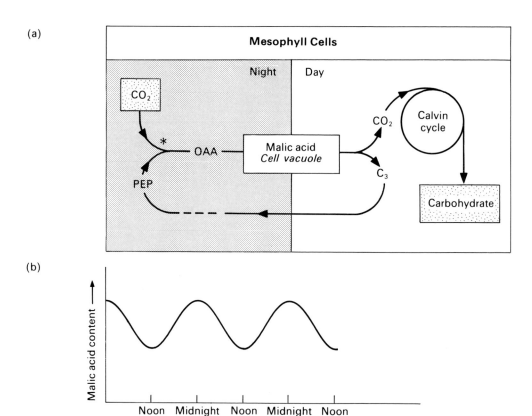

(a)

Mesophyll Cells

Night | Day

CO_2

* OAA — Malic acid *Cell vacuole*

PEP

CO_2

Calvin cycle

C_3

Carbohydrate

(b)

Malic acid content →

Noon Midnight Noon Midnight Noon

Figure 8.3 (a) At night the stomata are open and CO_2 is fixed by the action of PEP carboxylase (shown by an asterisk). Malic acid is stored in the cell vacuole. By day, with stomata shut, CO_2 is released from malic acid and fixed by the Calvin cycle. (b) Variation of malic acid in Crassulacean leaves.

■ CARBON DIOXIDE FIXATION IN CAM PLANTS

Cacti, succulents and other plants have evolved a CO_2 fixation system that permits them to survive in hot, dry environments that are extremely hostile to life. Water tension in both soil and air is often so low that many of these plants completely close their stomata during the day. This prevents what would be an otherwise intolerable water loss through transpiration but, of course, it also cuts off the supply of CO_2 for photosynthesis.

The solution to this difficulty is simple but effective: the stomata open at night when temperatures are much lower. During darkness, CO_2 is fixed by the same set of reactions that occur in the C_4 plants. Phosphoenolpyruvate carboxylase catalyses the

formation of oxaloacetic acid which is immediately reduced to malic acid. The latter is *stored in solution* in the cell vacuoles and the concentration of malic acid builds up during the night. Once daylight returns, the stomata close again and the CO_2 stored in malic acid is gradually released. This enters the Calvin cycle in the usual way – with the initial CO_2 fixation reaction being catalysed by RuBP carboxylase. Figure 8.3 shows the measured variation of malic acid concentration in a typical CAM plant and also summarises the arrangement described above.

Note that photorespiration is not a problem for CAM plants as the external oxygen-rich environment is closed off during the day. RuBP carboxylase operates in a sheltered environment of high CO_2 concentration, thus its oxygenase activity is minimal.

■ BIOCHEMICAL EXPLANATIONS OF SOME PHYSIOLOGICAL DATA

A continuing aim of this book has been to emphasise that the things we notice at the physiological level directly relate to the chemical reactions that happen inside cells. You have already met examples of this in animals, e.g. respiratory physiology, the homeostatic regulation of blood glucose and the temperature regulation system. The same close relationship between biochemistry and physiology also applies in plants.

Consider the experimental relationships shown in Fig. 8.4(a) and (b). These are for a C_3 plant such as wheat. The vertical axes show the rates of photosynthesis. These can be measured experimentally either in terms of the mass of CO_2 fixed per unit time (using radioactive $^{14}CO_2$) or volume of O_2 evolved. The horizontal axis shows in (a) the concentration of CO_2 in parts per million (ppm) and in (b) the intensity of illumination in joules of light energy incident per second on each m^2 of leaf.

These two plots provide an excellent example of what is often termed the *law of limiting factors*. This says that where several factors can affect the rate at which a process occurs, the actual rate is determined by whichever factor is the most limiting. In Fig. 8.4(a), plants illuminated by midday sun in temperate parts of the world receive around $350\,Jm^{-2}s^{-1}$ of light energy in the visible part of the electromagnetic spectrum. At this level of illumination, the *concentration of CO_2 is the limiting factor* over the range of CO_2 concentrations that give rise to the slope between A and B. Only at very high levels of CO_2 concentration (far above what occurs naturally) does the 'scene shift' so that *light intensity becomes the limiting factor* as shown by the plateau CD.

In Fig. 8.4(b) we have the other situation. In this plot, the constant level of CO_2 concentration is that which is naturally present in the atmosphere, i.e. around 300 ppm. In these circumstances, the intensity of illumination is rate limiting over a rather small range of light intensity: this gives slope PQ. For the species of plant shown in this graph, as soon as light intensity reaches $150\,Jm^{-2}s^{-1}$, photosynthesis can go no faster as shown by the plateau RS. At this point the concentration of CO_2 has become the limiting factor.

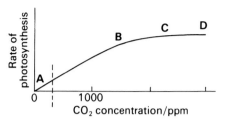

(a) Light intensity constant at $350\,Jm^{-2}s^{-1}$
   (= approximately midday summer sun in Europe)

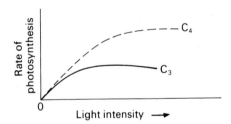

(b) $[CO_2] = 300$ ppm (= approximately atmospheric concentration)

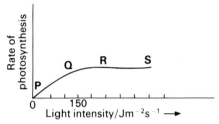

(c) $[CO_2] = 300$ ppm

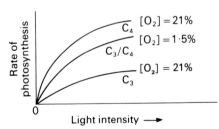

(d) C_3/C_4 comparisons at low and high oxygen concentrations

Figure 8.4 Factors affecting the rate of photosynthesis: the curves are discussed in the text. In graph (a), the dashed line shows the normal atmospheric concentration of CO_2. From the shape of the curve it is not surprising that horticulturalists blow carbon dioxide gas into greenhouses to increase the yield of tomatoes, lettuces, etc. Note also that graph (a) has implications for world vegetation if the increase in CO_2 concentration (associated with the greenhouse effect) continues. [Note that 300 parts per million is equal to 0.03%]

All of this can be explained biochemically. In Fig. 8.4(a), it looks as if the steady rise that occurs as CO_2 concentration increases (as shown by the curve AB) reflects the 'overwhelming availability' of ATP and NADPH produced by the massively illuminated light stage. All that is holding the plant back from making more and more carbohydrate is the availability of CO_2. Only at extraordinarily high levels of CO_2 does the availability of ATP and NADPH become limiting, giving rise to plateau CD. In Fig. 8.4(b), it is only in the dimmest of illumination that the availability of ATP and NADPH is rate limiting. Hence the slope PQ is short, and the plateau region RS, where CO_2 concentration is the limiting factor, is soon reached.

The explanation above is true enough in very simple terms. However, there is more to it than that as Fig. 8.4(c) shows. Here we have another plot of the rate of photosynthesis against light intensity. The lower line, for a typical C_3 plant, is very similar to that in (b). However, the upper line shows that C_4 plants can make much more use of the same limited supply of CO_2. This is exactly what one would expect from plants that have a system (the Hatch-Slack pathway) for *concentrating* CO_2 in the cells that have active RuBP carboxylase.

This idea makes us think again about Fig. 8.4(b) which was, remember, for a C_3 plant. Perhaps the fact that the line levels out as light increases is not simply because 'RuBP carboxylase can't go fast enough' but rather because (as light increases and the concentration of mesophyll CO_2 falls compared with O_2 concentration) RuBP carboxylase switches more and more to its carbohydrate-destroying oxygenase mode of action.

That this explanation is probably true is shown by Fig. 8.4(d). These are plots of the rate of photosynthesis against light intensity for C_3 and C_4 plants at *low* (i.e. non-natural) O_2 concentration *and* the rate of photosynthesis against light intensity for C_3 and C_4 plants at *high* (i.e. atmospheric) O_2 concentration. The results are exactly what you should expect from the biochemistry discussed earlier. When $[O_2] = 1.5\%$, there is no difference between C_3 and C_4 plants in their response to increasing light intensity. Why should there be? There is so little oxygen that photorespiration cannot be a problem. In contrast, at $[O_2] = 21\%$, there is a marked difference in the behaviour of the two kinds of plant: the C_4 type, with its power of concentrating CO_2 and protecting itself against high $[O_2]$, is more efficient than the C_3 plants.

■ NITROGEN FIXATION

Estimates for the whole planet indicate that, every year, some 200–300 million tonnes of nitrogen gas are taken from the atmosphere and are converted into ammonia or, more precisely, ammonium ions (NH_4^+). This conversion is called *nitrogen fixation*, and the chemistry of the process can be represented by the equation shown in Box B.

$$N_2 + 3XH_2 \longrightarrow 2NH_3 + 3X$$

Box B

This is a particularly interesting reaction in chemical terms and an absolutely vital reaction in terms of planetary life.

First, its chemical interest lies in the unlikeliness of it. Nitrogen is a very unreactive element; in fact the French for nitrogen is 'azote' which comes from the Greek *azoic* meaning 'lifeless'. This unreactivity stems from the high bond energy of the N≡N bond. It is hard to break this very stable triple bond and, in the industrial production of ammonia from nitrogen (the Haber-Bosch process), extreme physical conditions of temperature and pressure are required. In contrast, very many different species of bacteria are able to bring about the same reaction in the soil without heat and without excess pressure. Before we look at how they do this, consider first the importance of nitrogen fixation.

For most green plants the preferred source of nitrogen is nitrate. This is continually taken up by plant roots, reduced and then incorporated into organic compounds:

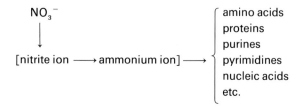

Figure 8.5 The fate of nitrate ions inside plant cells.

When the plant dies, all the nitrogenous compounds in the plant (listed on the right in Fig. 8.5 are some of the main ones) are re-oxidised in the soil to nitrate ions. This is the 'decomposer' part of the nitrogen cycle. You met some of the chemoautotrophic bacteria that bring about these reactions in Chapter 7. In theory, therefore, a steady cycle of uptake and regeneration occurs with nitrate reduction playing a key role.

Unfortunately, all does not usually go so smoothly because nitrogen is readily lost from this cycle. Denitrifying bacteria convert some nitrate to nitrogen gas. Much nitrate is leached into streams, rivers and then the sea and, thereby, entirely unavailable to the roots of land plants. In the sea itself there is some recycling in the upper layers of water. However, much organic nitrogen falls slowly to the bottom in the bodies of dead marine organisms. In the lifeless darkness of the depths of the oceans, these compounds remain permanently inaccessible for recycling.

Processes such as leaching would lead inevitably to a serious shortfall in combined nitrogen were it not for the continuous 'topping up' provided by nitrogen fixation. The vast mass of N_2 (four million billion tonnes) in the atmosphere provides an effectively limitless reserve.

There are three main contributing processes to the overall total of nitrogen fixation:

- biological fixation (by bacteria);
- industrial fixation (in fertiliser manufacture);
- atmospheric fixation (nitrogen oxide formation in lightning discharge).

These processes contribute to the annual total in the very approximate ratio of $3:1:1$ respectively, although nitrogen oxides released by the combustion of fossil fuels nowadays add a significant extra amount.

How does biological nitrogen fixation work? One key point is that *no* eukaryotic organism is (at present) able to fix nitrogen. Those bacteria that can fix nitrogen include: all the blue-green bacteria, some free-living aerobic bacteria such *Azotobacter*, some free-living strictly anaerobic bacteria such as *Clostridium* and, finally, bacteria living symbiotically with other organisms such as those that live in plant root nodules, e.g. *Rhizobium*.

In all these organisms nitrogen fixation is brought about by a very complex enzyme called *nitrogenase*.

This enzyme catalyses the reaction shown in Box B. The requirement for 'reducing power' (XH_2 in the box) is supplied in the blue-green bacteria directly by the light-dependent stage in photosynthesis. In the others, various catabolic reactions (different reactions for different species) provide what is necessary. ATP is also needed in quantity. The whole process can be written as shown in Box C.

From photosynthesis
    or catabolism
        ↓
$$N_2 + 3XH_2 + 6ATP \xrightarrow{\text{Nitrogenase}} 2NH_3 + 3X + 6ADP + 6P_i$$

Box C

The process of nitrogen fixation has been much researched because it is of such potential agricultural importance. The addition of industry-made nitrates to the soil to increase crop yield is increasingly necessary (as world population increases) but increasingly worrying because of the problems of *eutrophication* (i.e. depletion of oxygen from rivers, lakes, etc. caused by the overgrowth of organisms such as algae), drinking water contamination, and the energy cost of the ammonia-making industrial process.

The problem of world food supply would be transformed *if only* it were possible, through genetic engineering, either to (a) insert the nitrogenase-making bacterial genes into crop plants such as wheat, maize and rice, or (b) insert the genes that make possible symbiotic union and nodule formation into these major cereal crops. It may yet happen as much research is directed to these ends.

Difficulties abound, however. Not the least of these is that nitrogenase only works effectively in a strictly anaerobic environment. This causes no problem in the 'home bacteria', so to speak, because other biochemical features have evolved that ensure the environment remains anaerobic. Root nodules, for example, contain a pink, blood-like, pigment (called *leghaemoglobin*) that binds all free oxygen so making the nodule interior anaerobic.

POSTSCRIPT - METHODS IN BIOCHEMISTRY

CHAPTER 9

■ BIOCHEMICAL KNOWLEDGE

Open any biochemistry textbook and its pages are filled with metabolic pathways often confidently presented as undoubted truths. But, what do we mean by 'true'? It could mean one of several things . . . true in mammals but not in fish . . . a very complete story unlikely to change much with time . . . a partial story that has much still to be added to it . . . a scheme that seems likely now but turns out to be quite wrong or partially wrong in ten years' time. Once DNA was thought to make RNA but not vice versa. With the discovery of RNA viruses that, once inside their host cell, make DNA from the RNA template, that former 'truth' has now been qualified.

You know from Chapter 8 that different species of plants differ in their method of carbon dioxide fixation. Fish can safely excrete ammonia because of their aquatic environment whereas many mammals have to detoxify it by converting it to urea. There are many other examples of such differences, and you should continually ask yourself 'for which groups of organisms is this aspect of biochemistry true?' You should also consider why it is likely these biochemical differences have evolved. Many mammals would not survive if they did not posses the urea cycle; desert plants would not survive if they did not have the C_4 pathway. Biochemical detail, therefore, is not an incidental; it relates closely to the way of life of the organism.

As to the question of whether any description of a pathway is absolutely true or not, you ought to be aware that the 'scientific method' applies as much to biology and biochemistry as to any other science. Thus, *observations* of nature or of very preliminary experiments lead one to suggest a *hypothesis* (a theory about how something is happening). From that theory, the researcher is able to make some *predictions* which can be tested experimentally. From the results of those experiments, the hypothesis will be *supported* or *falsified*. However, 'falsification' does not usually mean the whole idea is abandoned; more likely it leads to some useful modification of the theory that can accommodate the new experimental results.

From this you can see that any set of 'facts' (perhaps the sequence of reactions that make up glycolysis) are really just 'ideas that have not been shown to be false'! Of course, where laboratory after laboratory gets the same results year after year, many hypotheses become so well supported that people become happy to consider them as facts.

■ THE ADVANCE OF BIOCHEMISTRY

In the period since the 1940s the growth of the subject has been enormous. But, a limiting factor to the growth of research is the amount of money that society is prepared to spend and the priority given to any one subject area in relation to others. This in its turn depends greatly on what *applied value* each subject area is thought to have to society. In the case of biochemistry, the list is clear enough: agriculture, food science, public health and medicine, are all vital in the task of keeping upwards of five billion humans alive. Biochemistry, along with its close 'cousins' such as molecular biology, immunology, biological chemistry, chemical microbiology, lies at the heart of our future well-being. More significantly, from a financial point of view, biochemistry is the scientific pivot of the drugs and agro-chemicals industries. These alone are worth thousands of millions of dollars world-wide and there are many other profitable businesses that depend on the applications of biochemistry.

Another limiting factor is the availability of experimental techniques. The growth of biochemical research has depended on the discovery of high-speed contrifugation, isotopic labelling of compounds, the development of electron microscopy and X-ray diffraction, the oxygen electrode, electrophoresis, chromatography and so on.

■ LOOKING AT ENTIRE CELLS

Light microscopy has played its part in scientific research since the primitive instruments of the seventeenth century. But, however good the quality of the lenses, no light microscope can ever give a clear magnification of more than 2000 times. This is because the *resolving power* of any microscope is about one half of the wavelength of the incident light. As the diameter of a typical bacterial cell is around 1000 nm, it is clear that limitations to the resolving power mean that little detail within such cells can be seen using ordinary light microscopes.

Enormous magnifications are possible using beams of electrons instead of light; a process known as *electron microscopy*. The photographic results are called *electron micrographs* (see photo 9.1).

Without electron microscopy (EM) it would not have been possible to relate chemical observations to the 'structural reality' of the cell. Earlier examples in this book, e.g. the fluid mosaic model of the cell membrane, and the structure and function of mitochondria and chloroplasts provide a few examples.

Special kinds of stain are used that react in a specific way with particular chemicals inside the cells. The stains help us to understand where certain substances are stored inside the cells and how these stores change. This technique of staining cell tissue is known as *histochemistry*.

■ LOOKING AT 'BROKEN UP' CELLS

The pictures of cell components within entire cells obtained by the various techniques of microscopy tell us nothing of the biochemical properties and biological function of these components. Somehow, we must be able to open up the cell without totally destroying it, separate out the nuclei, the mitochondria, the lysosomes, the ribosomes and all the other component particles, and finally, carry out experiments on the different cell fractions to discover what these components do and how they do it. The techniques involved are those of *cell homogenisation* and *cell fractionation*.

One way of homogenising tissue (e.g. a lump of liver) is to put it in some cold isotonic buffer and then to subject the mixture to the rending and tearing forces of a homogeniser (i.e. a machine that looks like an ordinary kitchen liquidiser). *Ultrasonics* can also be used to rupture cells.

The crucial requirement of any successful technique of homogenisation is that the *homogenate* (i.e. the tissue 'mashed' in buffer) should contain separated components that are still biochemically active. Thus, one must avoid any osmotic damage to delicate organelles. Enzymes and other proteins must be protected from thermal denaturation; and the natural pH value of the cell interior must be reproduced in the medium of the homogenate.

If particular organelles are needed for an investigation centrifugation can be used, particularly *high-speed centrifugation*. To obtain pure mitochondria from a plant cell homogenate, it is necessary to use a sequence of different spin times and rotor speeds (in revolutions per minute). This approach is called *differential centrifugation*. Cell walls and nuclei would be removed first using a *bench centrifuge*, then a short spin at moderate speed to remove chloroplasts, and finally a longer spin at greater *g* to produce a pellet of pure mitochondria. This pellet is then ready for resuspension in a medium that mimics the composition of cytoplasm.

Density gradient centrifugation, a rather special technique used to isolate macromolecules of different relative molecular masses, was referred to in

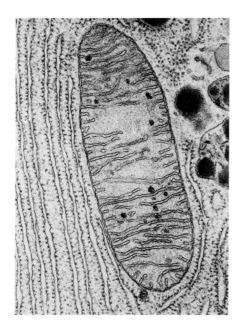

Photo 9.1 Electron micrograph of a mitochondrion.

Chapter 4 (page 49) when we described the Meselson and Stahl experiment. In the technique, tubes containing a gradient (i.e. an ever increasing concentration) of caesium chloride from top to bottom were used as the medium of centrifugation. DNA helixes of different mass (depending on whether one, both, or neither of the DNA strands were labelled with N^{15}) 'came to rest' in bands at various points down the tube.

■ MEASUREMENTS IN CELL PHYSIOLOGY AND BIOCHEMISTRY

Spectrophotometry (also called colorimetry in its simplest form) is a widespread technique and can be used to determine the concentration of very many different chemicals. More modern, more sensitive and easier to use is the *oxygen electrode*. This is a device containing a platinum electrode which produces an electrical voltage that is *directly proportional to oxygen concentration in the aqueous medium above the electrode*. It can be used in measuring the P:O ratio in mitochondria.

■ SEPARATING AND IDENTIFYING MOLECULES

The separation and identification of molecules can be carried out using techniques such as:

● electrophoresis;
● chromatography.

Some discussion of these techniques can be found in Chapter 2.

■ ISOTOPES IN BIOCHEMISTRY

Labelled compounds are used to work out what happens to molecules during metabolic processes. The importance of *isotopic labelling* as a technique can not be over-emphasised. Here are some examples:

● much of what is known about protein synthesis has resulted from the use of radioactive amino acids;
● many details of carbohydrate and fat catabolism are based on experiments using labelled compounds supplied to tissues as fuel;
● many of the details of the Calvin cycle became clear through the use of labelled carbon dioxide;
● the use of labelled DNA provided conclusive evidence for semi-conservative replication (see text and Appendix).

■ CONCLUSIONS

One aim of this final chapter has been to mention the different techniques you 'ought' to know about. However, another goal of almost equal importance has been to give you an outline of the nature of biochemical research. All the basic facts, theories and pathways of earlier chapters have largely been presented without the experimental evidence on which they are based. We hope you now have some insight into how investigation and biochemical discovery proceeds.

As was said in Chapter 1, the whole subject of biochemistry is difficult enough to warrant an unusual presentation. Thus we have tried to make plain any relationships to other parts of biology and we have used a range of longer than usual explanations to make clear what is so often unclear. Chapter 1 posed a number of questions which any thoughtful student of biology at this level should be able to answer, at least in part. You now should be able to do that.

The factual matter contained in the nine chapters covers all that is likely to be asked of you – on things biochemical – in your exams. Often the text offers you slightly more than the minimum. In doing this, the intention is not to overload you but to provide that 'bit extra' which makes for better understanding – and slightly better answers, too. Good luck!

A GUIDE TO CHEMISTRY

In order to understand the chemistry of life, you first of all need a basic knowledge of chemistry itself. If you have this knowledge already, you will probably still find it useful to flip through this section as many links between chemical principles and biological systems are introduced. You should certainly read the information on water relationships as this is explained in some depth. If your chemistry is rather rusty, a thorough reading of the following pages should definitely help. It won't make you an expert, but it will assist you in understanding the rest of this book.

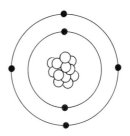

Figure 1 Simple diagram of an atom. This one is carbon with six protons and six neutrons in the nucleus, and six electrons in orbit around them. The orbits really represent the energy levels of the electrons in them.

■ ELEMENTS

All matter in the universe is made up of elements. There are 109 elements altogether although not all of these occur naturally (nuclear physicists have managed to make some). Quite a large number of these are found in living systems and biologically the most significant ones are carbon (C), hydrogen (H), oxygen (O), nitrogen (N), phosphorus (P) and sulphur (S). All elements are made up of *atoms*.

■ ATOMS

Atoms themselves consist of three basic particles, i.e. those with a positive charge (*protons*) those with no charge (*neutrons*), and much smaller particles with a negative charge (*electrons*). Very simply, the protons and neutrons of an atom are clustered at the centre (the *nucleus*), with the electrons orbiting around them. Each orbit will only hold a certain number of electrons, for example the innermost will hold a maximum of two, the next one eight, and so on. For greatest stability of the atom, an orbit should be filled. Electrons can also be 'boosted' from an inner orbit to an outer one by an input energy and you will see the importance of this in photosynthesis.

The number of protons in the nucleus is unique for each element, and is known as the *atomic number*.

This is often written as a subscript next to the symbol for the element.

To get an idea of the size of the atom, the number of protons and neutrons are added together to give the *atomic mass* (these two particles are each regarded as having a mass of one while electrons are too small to make any difference). The atomic mass can be written as a superscript alongside the element symbol. For example, in the case of a carbon atom with six protons and six neutrons we would represent it as follows: $^{12}_{6}C$.

As the number of protons in an atom is the same as the number of electrons, the atom is neutral. However, electrons can be gained or lost. If the atom gains electrons it becomes negatively charged, if it loses electrons it becomes positively charged. A charged atom is known as an *ion*. Examples include the sodium ion (Na^+), chloride ion (Cl^-) and magnesium ion (Mg^{2+}, i.e. two electrons lost).

Although the number of protons in an element is always the same, the number of neutrons can and does vary. These variants are known as isotopes.

Isotopes of an element have the same atomic number but different mass numbers. Hydrogen, for example, exists as three isotopes: ordinary hydrogen, deuterium and tritium. All contain one proton per nucleus (which is what makes them hydrogen) but, respectively, have no neutron, one neutron and two neutrons per nucleus. It is normal in biology to show just the mass number, thus: ^1H, ^2H and ^3H.

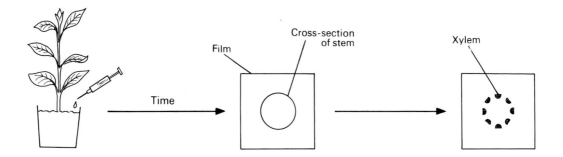

Figure 2 Using a radioactive tracer. The plant is given water with radioactive ^{18}O isotope. The stem is cut into sections, which are then placed on photographic film. The stem section is then removed. Location of fogging matches location of xylem in the stem, i.e. strong evidence that xylem is the tissue that transports water up the stem.

The basis of isotopic labelling is that, for a given element, some isotopes are 'unusual' and so can be used to *label* a molecule. The method also depends on the fact that molecules containing the unusual isotope react in an entirely normal way, but can be detected by the experimenter through the unusual physical properties of the isotopic atom. Most easily detected are the isotopes that are *radioactive*. These emit radiation of one or more types that can be detected by an appropriate kind of counter such as a Geiger-Müller counter or by their ability to fog photographic film.

The most frequently used isotope is ^{14}C. This weak β-emitter has been used to label many different compounds of carbon. It is easy to detect and relatively inexpensive to produce in an atomic pile and then incorporate into particular organic compounds or, indeed, $^{14}CO_2$.

Other isotopes are *non-radioactive* and differ from the common type of atom solely because they have an unusual mass. Unfortunately, some of the most important elements in biochemistry research do not have radioactive isotopes, nitrogen and oxygen are prime examples. These molecules can be labelled with ^{18}O instead of ^{16}O or ^{15}N instead of ^{14}N, but the label is much harder to detect and methods are therefore much less sensitive. You have already met, in some detail, an example of the use of a non-radioactive isotope, i.e. the use of ^{15}N in the Meselson and Stahl experiment. (See Chapter 4).

■ MOLECULES

Atoms can combine together to form molecules. There are different ways in which this can happen, but all involve activity on the part of the electrons. There are two main ways in which atoms join together. These are:

● covalent bonding;
● ionic bonding.

■ Covalent bonding

This is where two or more atoms *share* electrons, so that the outermost electron orbit of each is filled and stable. For example, an oxygen atom can combine with two hydrogen atoms to form water. The outer orbit of the oxygen atom now has a stable eight

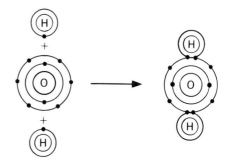

Figure 3 Hydrogen combining covalently with oxygen to form water. The orbits of the atoms are filled through the sharing of electrons.

electrons and the hydrogen atom a stable two electrons.

Ionic bonding

This occurs when one atom donates electrons to another atom. As a result, the first atom loses a negative charge and so becomes positive, the second gains a negative charge, and so opposite charges attract each other the atoms are firmly bound together. The outer electron orbit of each atom is also filled. For example, a sodium atom can donate an electron to a chlorine atom to form sodium chloride (common salt).

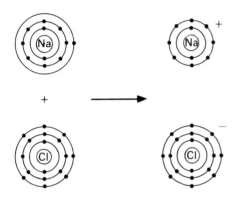

Figure 4 Sodium combining ionically with chlorine. The sodium atom loses an electron, the chlorine gains it. The orbits of each atom are now full.

The atoms which make up a molecule may be the same, e.g. H_2, O_2, or different, e.g. CO_2, $C_6H_{12}O_6$. The subscript number tells you how many atoms of that type there are in the molecule.

In order to make a stable molecule, atoms must form a certain number of bonds. Carbon, for example, must have four bonds, oxygen two and hydrogen one. In diagrams, the bonds are shown as lines. When one pair of electrons is shared, a *single bond* is formed. When two pairs of electrons are shared, a so-called *double bond* is formed. This tends to be less stable and so more reactive than a single bond.

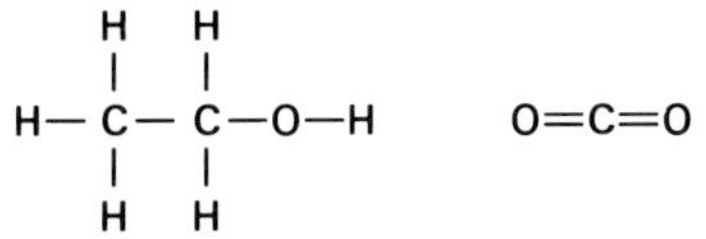

$$
\begin{array}{c}
\overset{\displaystyle H}{\underset{\displaystyle H}{|}} \quad \overset{\displaystyle H}{\underset{\displaystyle H}{|}} \\
H-C-C-O-H \\
\end{array}
\qquad O{=}C{=}O
$$

Ethanol   Carbon dioxide

Figure 5

CHEMICAL REACTIONS

A chemical reaction involves a change in one or more molecules. This might be adding one molecule to another, splitting a large molecule into smaller ones, changing the positions of atoms inside a molecule, etc. For example:

$$C_6H_{12}O_6 + 6O_2 \longrightarrow 6CO_2 + 6H_2O$$

Note that the equation is balanced, i.e. you always end up with the same number of atoms that you started out with. The large numbers in the equation identify how many molecules of that type are taking part in or being formed by the reaction (i.e. $6CO_2$ means six molecules of carbon dioxide).

In biological systems many of the reactions are reversible, and this is indicated by the symbol $\rightleftharpoons$ instead of an arrow.

One other point about biological systems. For various reasons, the reactions tend to occur in pathways such as:

$$A \rightarrow B \rightarrow C \rightarrow D \rightarrow E \rightarrow F \rightarrow G \rightarrow H$$

Furthermore, the pathways tend to have branches coming off them and joining onto other pathways. The result is enormous flexibility, as a chemical can be diverted into different pathways according to the cell's needs, but creates immense problems of control. (See Chapter 3).

All chemical reactions involve the breaking of bonds and the making of new bonds, and all reactions involve changes in energy.

ENERGY AND CHEMICAL REACTIONS

Energy is defined as the capacity to do work. There are various types of energy such as light energy, nuclear energy, kinetic energy, potential energy (the potential of a system to do work), heat energy and chemical energy. Each chemical can be regarded as having a certain amount of potential energy which is released only when it reacts. *The First Law of Thermodynamics* states that energy can neither be created nor destroyed, only converted from one form to another. If this is so, what happens when the potential energy level of the *products* of a reaction is lower than that of the *reactants*?

The answer must be that the 'excess' energy is given out in some form, usually as heat. These are known as *exergonic* reactions. Similarly, if the potential energy level of the products is higher than that of the reactants, energy must be fed into the system in some form in order for the reaction to occur. This is an *endergonic* reaction. Energy change from one form to another (e.g. light energy to chemical energy in photosynthesis) is known as transduction.

Another interesting point about biological systems is that the energy given out from exergonic reactions in the cell is used to drive the endergonic reactions. (This is discussed in more detail later.)

■ ACIDS AND BASES

An acid is a substance which when put into water acts as a source of hydrogen ions. For example:

$$HCl \rightleftharpoons H^+ + Cl^-$$

As hydrochloric acid dissociates very readily in water into H^+ and Cl^- ions, it can be regarded as being a *strong acid*. The more usual acids found in living systems are those organic acids which possess a carboxylic acid group (—COOH). These acids don't dissociate so readily, and so are regarded as *weak acids*.

A base is a chemical which has a tendency to accept hydrogen ions often by the base itself dissociating into ions, followed by one of these ions associating with the H^+.

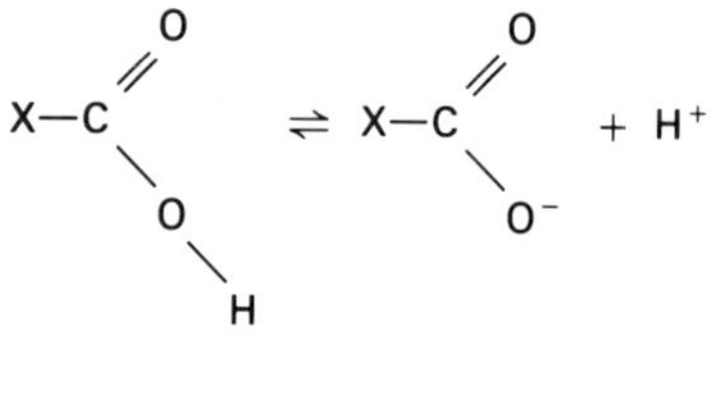

Figure 6 Carboxylic acid dissociating.

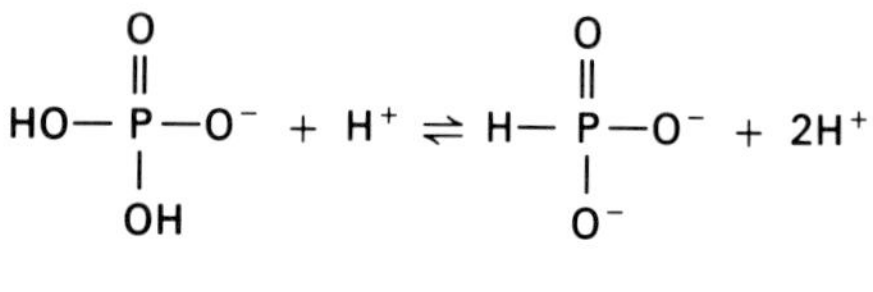

Figure 7 Phosphate salt dissociating and combining with H^+.

The level of acidity or basicity (usually known as alkalinity) of a solution is measured by using the pH scale, which is the negative logarithm of the concentration of hydrogen ions. Don't worry too much about understanding this, just remember that the scale runs from 0 to 14. At the midpoint, 7, the pH of the solution is neutral. Below 7, it acidic, above 7 it is alkaline. The further away from 7 the pH of the solution is, the higher the level of acidity/alkalinity.

It is highly undesirable to have fluctuations in the pH level of living organisms. To prevent any fluctuations, certain chemical substances known as *buffers* are present. These resist changes in pH by mopping up any excess H+ ions present, and releasing them when the pH level falls. Blood proteins, especially haemoglobin, are essential for this purpose.

■ DIFFUSION, OSMOSIS AND WATER POTENTIAL

Diffusion is the net movement of particles of a substance (e.g. molecules and ions) from an area of high concentration to an area of low concentration, i.e. movement *down* a concentration gradient. The larger the difference in concentrations the steeper the gradient and the faster diffusion will occur. The particles move because they possess a certain amount of kinetic energy. In fact, you could think of diffusion as being the movement of particles from a high kinetic energy area to a lower kinetic energy area for the particular substance. Diffusion will keep happening until the concentration of the substance, and thus its kinetic energy level in the system, is even.

Many substances enter or leave cells by diffusion. In some cases, cell membranes have structures such as pores to allow easier movement of particular molecules across them, e.g. glucose molecules into red blood cells. This is known as *facilitated diffusion*.

Osmosis is a special case of diffusion. It is the movement of water from a dilute solution to a concentrated solution across a selectively permeable membrane. Look at Fig. 8 carefully.

The membrane is permeable to water but not to anything dissolved in the water. On one side of the membrane is a dilute solution, on the other is a concentrated solution.

Remember that the water molecules on both sides of the membrane will have kinetic energy and so be

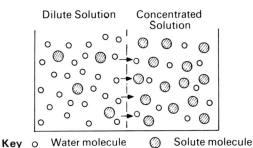

Key o Water molecule   ⊘ Solute molecule

Figure 8 Osmosis. Water molecules will move along a diffusion gradient (i.e. from left to right in this diagram).

moving around. The more energy they have, the greater the amount of movement. This means that the water molecules will frequently strike the membrane where there is a pore and so pass through to the other side.

So why should there be an overall movement of water from the dilute to the concentrated side? The answer lies in the presence of the dissolved substance. On the dilute solution side, the main factor interfering with the movement of water is collision with other water molecules. On the concentrated solution side, the water molecules will be in collision with the dissolved molecules as well as other water molecules. However, as you will have seen in Chapter 2, the water molecules are also attracted to the dissolved substance, so cutting down their kinetic energy. The more substance dissolved, the less kinetic energy there is in the water molecules. As diffusion of a substance occurs from areas of high kinetic energy to areas of low kinetic energy, the water molecules will move from the dilute to the concentrated solution until the kinetic energy of the molecules is evenly distributed on both sides of the membrane. The amount of kinetic energy of water molecules in an area is described in terms of the

water potential (ψ). Pure water at one atmosphere of pressure (1 atm) is given a water potential of zero, so all solutions will have negative values (i.e. value *less than* that of pure water).

When two solutions are separated by a selectively permeable membrane, water will always move from the solution with the less negative water potential to the solution with the more negative water potential.

Osmosis is of major importance to living systems. In animals, if the fluid in which the cells are bathed is not of exactly the same concentration as the cells' protoplasm, water will either move in or out of the cell with lethal results. Therefore, animals need to have a system of *osmoregulation* to make sure that the tissue fluid concentration remains constant. This is true of organisms such as *Amoeba*, with their contractile vacuoles expelling the water taken in by osmosis, right through to mammals with their complex fluid-monitoring system in the brain working in cooperation with highly effective filters in the kidneys. Maintaining this constant level of fluid concentration is an example of *homeostasis*.

With plants, there is a different situation. As long as they have a plentiful supply of water via the roots, the cellulose cell wall prevents the cells from bursting (see Fig. 9).

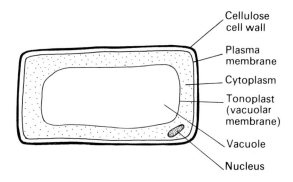

Cellulose cell wall

Plasma membrane

Cytoplasm

Tonoplast (vacuolar membrane)

Vacuole

Nucleus

Figure 9 Generalised plant cell.

FURTHER QUESTIONS

1. What do you understand by the terms (i) radio-active tracer and (ii) metabolic pathway? Describe how the use of radioactive tracers has improved our knowledge of a named metabolic pathway. (*London A 1990*)

2. (a) Chloroplasts from spinach were broken open and then separated into membranous and soluble fractions, labelled M and S respectively. Both fractions were found to be biochemically active. In which of these fractions would you find the following? In each case give a reason for your answer: (i) chlorophyll (ii) carbon dioxide converted to glucose, (iii) oxygen produced from water.
(b) Make a large drawing to show the internal structure of a mitochondrion. Show clearly on your drawing the site of the following processes: (i) tricarboxylic acid cycle, (ii) electron transfer chain. Indicate the approximate scale of your drawing. (*COSSEC AS 1990*)

3. (a) Explain the effect of increasing temperature on enzyme activity (i) from 0°C–37°C, (ii) above 37°C.
(b) Fill in the missing words in the text below.
Enzymes are a type of protein known as _____ proteins. The sequence of _____ _____ determines the _____ structure. The precise shape of the protein is known as the _____ structure. The energy of activation of the reaction is _____ by the enzyme due to the formation of a complex between the _____ and the enzyme at a site known as the _____ _____. The precise _____ of this results in enzyme specificity. (*COSSEC AS 1990*)

4. Give an account of (a) the fluid mosaic model of cell membrane structure and (b) the different functions of the membranes of cells and their organelles. How do these functions relate to the structure of the membrane? (*JMB A Nuffield Biology 1989*)

5. (a) Explain the meaning of the term 'cellular respiration'.

(b) Describe the part played by each of the following in cellular respiration: (i) glycogen, (ii) fermentation, (iii) oxidative phosphorylation.
(c) What are the roles of electron transport systems in cell metabolism? (*London A 1988*)

6. Write an account of the dark reaction in photosynthesis and explain how radioactive tracers have been used to study this pathway. (*London A 1988*)

7. Briefly state the evidence that indicates that the oxygen evolved in photosynthesis is released from water. Explain how the energy of light is converted to the chemical energy of ATP. Why are the reactions involving the reduction of fixed CO_2 often referred to as 'dark reactions'? Name the compound which initially accepts CO_2 in C_3 photosynthesis. Briefly describe how C_4 plants differ in the initial stages of carbon dioxide fixation. State three physiological advantages to the plant of the C_4 pathway. What is the reducing power of $NADPH_2$ used for in the chloroplast? (*Cambridge International A 1990*)

8. (a) Briefly explain the terms 'endergonic reaction' and 'exergonic reaction' and give an example of each in living organisms. (b) Some strongly exergonic reactions occur only very slowly. How does an understanding of 'activation energy' explain this? (*Oxford AS 1989*)

9. State the significant chemical features and then explain the biological importance of the following molecules: (i) phospholipid and (ii) ATP. (*Cambridge International A 1990*)

10. Describe the structure of a mitochondrion and give an account of the chemistry and importance of the cytochrome system. (*Scotland CSYS 1989*)

11. Give an account of the structure of DNA and its control of protein synthesis within a cell. (*Scotland Higher 1989*)

Note: where a page number for a word is shown in bold print, an explanation or definition can be found in the text